The Great Gatsby
了不起的盖茨比

原著 F. Scott Fitzgerald

[美] F·斯科特·菲茨杰拉德

改编 Daniel Barney

翻译 许洪珍

主审 李安林

航空工业出版社

图书在版编目(CIP)数据

床头灯英语学习读本 I/毛荣贵等主编.
－北京:航空工业出版社,2004.5
ISBN 7-80183-349-X

Ⅰ.床… Ⅱ.毛… Ⅲ.英语-高等学校-水平
考试-自学参考资料 Ⅳ.H310.42

中国版本图书馆 CIP 数据核字(2004)第 026603 号

航空工业出版社出版发行
(北京市安定门外小关东里 14 号　100029)

北京富生印刷厂　　　　全国各地新华书店经销
2004 年 5 月第 1 版　　　2004 年 7 月第 2 次印刷
开本:787×1092　1/32　印张:77.5　字数:1650 千字
印数:8001～12000　　　(全 10 册)定价:100.00 元

本社图书如有缺页、倒页、脱页、残页等情况,请与本社发行
部联系负责调换。联系电话:64890262　84917422

写在前面的话

——中国人学英语现状分析

◆英语是语言的帝国

全球 60 亿人中,有 8 亿人的母语是英语;2.5 亿人的第二母语是英语。12.3 亿人学习英语,33.6 亿人和英语有关。全世界电视节目的 75%、E-mail 的 80%、网络的 85%、软件源代码的 100%使用英语。40~50 年后,全球 50%的人精通英语。全球约 6000 种语言,本世纪末 90%将消亡。届时英语作为主导语言的地位将进一步得到提升。

目前中国大约有 3 亿人在学英语,超过英国和美国的人口总和,这是中国努力与时代接轨、与国际接轨的一个重要标志。大量中国人熟练掌握国际通用语言是中华民族走向繁荣富强的必要保障。

◆英语学习的远期目标

在中国英语已经远远超过一个学科的范畴,一个人英语水平的高低总是和事业、前途、地位,甚至命运联系在一起。对于个人来讲,英语在人生旅途中具有战略意义,不失时机地在英语上投入时间、投入精力、投入金钱符合与时俱进的潮流,是明智之举。

◆目前存在的问题

尽管在中国学习英语的人数众多,但收效却令人担忧,学了这么多年英语,能够运用自如的人实在是凤毛麟角。由于运用能力差,无法品尝到英语学习成功的快乐,很多人不得不承认学英语的目的只能是学英语,这就是人们常说的"为了学英语而学英语"。

◆考试的压力对英语学习的积极影响

在我国与个人命运休戚相关的各类考试,如中考、高考、四六级、硕士研究生入学考试、博士研究生入学考试、职称考试、出国考试,都考或只考英语。目前很多人把中国人学不好英语的责任推到英语考试身上，好像中国人学不好英语就是因为有了英语考试，甚至有人还产生了将英语考试废除的想法。

大家可以冷静地反思一下：如果没有各种各样的英语考试，哪里有这么多中国人坚持学英语？国家正是利用了考试这个指挥棒引导很多人去学英语。说句实话，你不能指望每个中国人都怀着与国际接轨的远大抱负去学英语。中国曾经取消过考试，结果造成了人才 10 年的断层。所以我的看法是在谈论考试的不足时，首先应该承认它在选拔人才、培养人才方面的不可替代的作用。英语考试对中国人学英语起到了很大的积极作用，功不可没。但必须承认：如果真想把英语学好，光会做几道考试题是远远不够的。

◈ 不可缺少的环节

没有几百万字的输入无法学好英语。语言的习得是一个长期的过程，需要大量的"输入"。一个由汉语武装起来的头脑，没有几百万字英文的输入，即使要达到一般水平也难。绝大多数的英语学习者正是由于缺少了这一环节，所以停留在一个无奈的水平上。

◈ "圣人"学英语的做法

在学英语的长远目标和考试的压力共同作用下自然会产生学好英语的强烈愿望，但这一愿望的实现需要有很强的"韧劲"（自我约束力）。春来不是读书天，夏日炎炎正好眠，秋有蚊虫冬又冷，收起书包待明年。随着物质文明的繁荣，总有一些理由使人不能安心学习。这样下去，我们的英语之树永远长不高。古人云：人静而后安，安而能后定，定而能后慧，慧而能后悟，悟而能后得。很有道理。在四川大足佛教石刻艺术中，有一组大型佛雕《牧牛图》，描绘了一个牧童和牛由斗争、对抗到逐渐协调、融合，最后合而为一的故事。佛祖说："人的心魔难伏，就像牛一样，私心杂念太多太多；修行者就要像牧童，修炼他们，驯服他们，以完美自己的人生。"那些具有很强的心力的人，我们姑且称其为"圣人"，他们能够驯服那些影响我们学习的大牛、小牛，抵制各种诱惑，集中精力,专心学习,到达成功的彼岸。

◈凡人的困惑

在目前的教育体系中,学好英语是需要坚韧不拔的毅力的。但问题是我们大多数平凡的人无法和圣人相比,所以在学英语的征途上,失败者多,成功者少。客观地讲,在中国英语学习的失败率应该在 99% 以上,即使采用不是太高的标准来衡量——原因是英语的门槛太高了。有的人说难道我们不能把所有的或者是大多数的人都变成圣人吗,这样大多数人就可以学好英语了。我们不得不承认大多数凡夫俗子是不能够成为圣人的。值得我们深思的是目前的英语学习体系中没有给大多数人提供一条平坦的道路。

◈兴趣——英语学习成功的真正源泉

我和大家一样都是凡人,我也曾经遇到过学英语的困惑,干巴巴的课文无论怎样都激不起我的兴趣。幸运的是我有一个在国外生活多年的姐姐,有一次她回国,给我带来很多浅显有趣的读物。我拿起一本一读,觉得很简单,一个星期就读完了。就英语学习而言,一部英文小说其实就是用英语建构的一个"虚拟世界"。那里有人,有人的心灵和人与人之间关系的揭示,有人与自然、与社会的冲突和调和。走进一部英文小说,你实际上就已经"生活"在一个"英语世界"里了,不愁没有东西可学。经典作品要读,写得好的当代通俗小说也要读。我一共读了 50本,从此对英语产生了兴趣,英语水平有了很大的提高。还是爱因斯坦说得好:"兴趣是最好的老师。"

◈《新概念英语》的主编 L. G. Alexander 的启示

中国人读英语书有个特点,越读不懂越读,习惯于读满篇都是生词的文章。L. G. Alexander 先生是世界著名的英语教学专家,他的经典之作《新概念英语》对于中国的英语教学产生了深远的影响。针对这一现状 Alexander 先生说过,"记住,你的接受型词汇量(即你听或阅读英语时能理解的部分)比你的积极词汇量(即你在说或写时能自如运用的部分)要大得多。如果要扩大词汇量,最好的办法是多听英语,多读英语,但不要超出自己的水平,阅读那些比你目前水平稍低的书。"这才是提高英语运用能力的诀窍。

本套读物的特色:

●情节曲折:本书选材的时候非常注意作品的吸引力。比方说:

《查泰莱夫人的情人》(Lady Chatterley's Lover):我当年读大学的时候,班上每个同学都买一本看。有的同学甚至熄灯后,打着手电筒躲在被窝里看。

《吸血鬼》(Dracula):这个故事真吓人,我看完以后好几天没睡好觉。后来我的一个学生说他对英语从来不感兴趣,我就把这本小说推荐给他。后来他对我说:"这是我一口气读完的第一本英语书,就是太吓人了。老师,能不能再给我来一本?"

《呼啸山庄》(Wuthering Heights):讲述的是一个骇人听闻的复仇故事,当初没有想到这本书的作者竟然是一个生活在几乎与世隔绝环境中的女孩。

《飘》(Gone with the Wind):几乎所有的美国女孩都读过这本书,主人公斯佳丽是美国女孩的偶像,可以说我见过的每个美国女孩都是一个 Scarlett.

……

本套丛书中包含的都是在你一生中值得去读的作品,读这些作品不但可以提高你的英语水平,而且能够提高你的个人修养。

●语言地道:本套读物均由美国作家执笔,用流畅的现代英语写成。他们写作功底深厚,这是母语为非英语的作者很难达到的。

●通俗易懂:本书是用 3300 个最常用的英语单词写成,易读懂,对于难词均有注释,而且采用英汉对照的形式。你躺在床上不用翻字典就能顺利地读下去。

●配有高质量的音带:这样大家可以在读懂的基础上进行听的训练,请注意:阅读需要量,听力更需要量。大量的语音输入是用英语深入交谈的源泉。

这套读物供你在下课后或下班后闲暇时阅读，她的优点是帮你实现英语学习的生活化，使英语成为你生活的一部分。这才是英语成功的真谛，更是任何有难度事情成功的真谛。

王若平　于北京

本系列丛书学习指导咨询中心：
北京通向未来语言研究所
地　址:北京市海淀区清华南路华清商务会馆 1501 室
邮　编:100083
E - mail:wrx1@vip. sina. com
网　址:www. sinoexam. com

故 事 梗 概

《了不起的盖茨比》是美国著名小说家弗·司各特·菲茨杰拉德（F. Scott Fitzgerald, 1896—1940）以完美的艺术形式表现的关于"美国梦"的幻灭这一主题思想的一部力作，发表于 1925 年。

小说的背景被设定在现代化的美国社会中上阶层的白人圈内，通过卡拉韦的叙述展开。卡拉韦出生于美国中西部，后来到美国纽约学习经营股票生意，并想以此发财。他住在长岛，与故事的主人公盖茨比为邻，并与之交上了朋友。盖茨比原名盖茨，和卡拉韦一样也来自中西部，他出身贫苦，但雄心勃勃，后因贩卖私酒而暴富。他经常在家举办大型豪华聚会，大宴宾客，以显示其阔绰，目的是为了吸引五年前的恋人黛西并赢回她的芳心。五年前在盖茨比服兵役时黛西曾是他的恋人，在盖茨比去海外参加第一次世界大战期间，由于利欲熏心嫁给了出身于富豪家庭的纨绔子弟汤姆·布坎南。然而物欲和肉欲的满足并没能填补黛西精神上的空虚与贫乏。在卡拉韦的帮助下，与盖茨比重逢后好像又旧情复燃。但黛西已不是原来的黛西，她不再是盖茨比想象中的纯情女孩，而是一个愚蠢、自私、庸俗、美丽的躯壳。盖茨比的美丽旧梦终于被打碎了，但他还在做最后的挣扎，仍对黛西抱有一丝幻想，以至遭遇了更加凄惨可悲的结局。后来黛西在一次酒后驾驶盖茨比的车时轧死了汤姆的情妇，却与汤姆一道密谋并残忍地嫁祸于盖茨比，导致死者的丈夫突然闯入盖茨比家中并开枪打死了盖茨比，然后自杀身亡，使盖茨比最终彻底成为自私而残忍的黛西的牺牲品。卡拉韦与仅有的几位朋友参加了盖茨比的葬礼，这与他生前上百人的豪华聚会形成了巨大的反差。参加完盖茨比的葬礼之后，卡拉韦决定返回中西部的家，远离喧嚣、冷漠、空洞、虚假的东部大都市。

目　　录

Chapter One　Arriving in West Egg ············· (2)

第一章　到达西卵镇 ·························· (3)

Chapter Two　Tom's Other Woman ············· (32)

第二章　汤姆的另一个女人 ·················· (33)

Chapter Three　My Strange Neighbor ··········· (48)

第三章　我的奇怪邻居 ······················ (49)

Chapter Four　Daisy and Gatsby ·············· (72)

第四章　黛西与盖茨比 ······················ (73)

Chapter Five　A Tea Party ·················· (96)

第五章　一次茶会 ·························· (97)

Chapter Six　The Big Party ·················· (120)

第六章　大型聚会 ·························· (121)

Chapter Seven　An Afternoon Together ········· (140)

第七章　共度下午 ·························· (141)

Chapter Eight　The Yellow Car ··············· (168)

第八章　黄色轿车 ·························· (169)

Chapter Nine　The Murder ·················· (178)

第九章　谋杀 ······························ (179)

Chapter Ten　The Great Gatsby ·············· (194)

第十章　了不起的盖茨比 ···················· (195)

CHAPTER ONE Arriving in West Egg

I still don't know why, but it is hard for people from *the Midwest* to live in the big cities of the East. Perhaps the Midwest is too much in our blood. I left the East and came back to my hometown last fall, after only six months in New York I was tired of it. I returned to this Midwestern city where I was a child. My family name is Carraway and my name is Nick. The Carraway family has been living in the Midwest for more than seventy years. My grandfather's brother was the first one to come to the Midwest. He came in 1851 and opened the business that my father still does today.

I graduated from university in 1915. I attended New Haven University, the same university that my father attended twenty-five years before. After university I went over to Europe to fight in the *Great War*. I feel in love with Europe and felt a great energy inside me when I was there. When I came back to the Midwest it felt too small. Instead of feeling that the Midwest was the warm center of the world, the Middle West now seemed like its far edge. So I decided to go to New York City, the most modern city of the East, and study the business of buying and selling bonds. Many of my friends from university were working selling bonds; I decided that I would follow them and do the same. My father said that he would give me money to live in New York for one year and in the spring of 1922 I

第一章　到达西卵镇

我至今仍不清楚从中西部地区来的人为什么难以适应在东部大城市的生活，也许是因为在我们的血液里中西部情结太多的缘故吧。在纽约只呆了六个月，我就烦了，于是去年秋天我离开东部回到了家乡，回到了年少时的这个中西部城市。我姓卡拉韦，名字叫尼克。我们卡拉韦家族生活在中西部地区已经七十多年了。我祖父的一个兄弟最先来到中西部，他1851年来了以后开始经营一项生意，至今现在我父亲还在经营着。

我1915年大学毕业。我上的是纽黑文大学，是二十五年前我父亲读过的同一所大学。毕业后我去欧洲参加了世界大战。我喜欢欧洲，在那儿我觉得心里有股巨大的力量。回到中西部后我觉得这里太小，不再感觉到中西部是世界温暖地带的中心，却觉着这里是世界的最边缘。因此我决定到东部最现代化的城市——纽约去学做股票交易。大学时的许多朋友都在做债券生意，我便决定跟着他们干。父亲说将给我够在纽约住一年的钱，于是在1922年春我搬到那儿——我相信我会在那儿永远待下去的。

the Midwest = the Middle West 美国中西部

Midwest *adj.*美国中西部的 *n.*[总称]美国中西部的人，美国中西部文化(或社会习俗等)。

Great War 即 Great World War Ⅰ，1914–1918的第一次世界大战。

moved there — I believed that I would stay there forever.

At first I had wanted to find a room inside New York City, but then I felt that I would miss the green trees and open yards, so when a young man at the office suggested that we rent a house together outside of the city, it sounded like a good idea. We found a small house to rent for only eighty dollars a month. However, just after we rented the house our office ordered him to go to work in Washington, and I *went rented* the house alone. I had an old car; it was a Dodge. I also hired a European woman from my new village to come to make my bed and cook my breakfast. I felt lonely the first few days until one morning *some* man, who had just arived in the village, stopped me while I was walking down the road.

"How do I get to West Egg village?" he asked, very tired.

I told him. And I was happy to learn that I was not the *newest* person in town now; I was now a guide. As I walked home the sun was shining and the trees were full of thick, green leaves, I felt that my life was starting again with the summer.

I read a lot during that summer. I bought a lot of books about banking and money affairs. All the books sat on my bookshelf looking very important. They promised to tell me the secrets of becoming rich. I planned to read so many books. When I was in university I was very interested in literature,

起初，我曾想在纽约市内找一间房子，但我觉得那会看不到绿树和开阔的院子，因此当办公室的一个年轻人提议我们在市郊合租一套房子时，我觉得倒是个好主意。我们找到了一处小房子，每月租金只有80美元。然而就在刚租下房子后，我们公司就派他去华盛顿工作，我只好一个人租住了这套房子。我有辆旧车，是辆道奇。我又从新到的村里雇了个欧洲妇女，为我整理床铺、做早餐。开始的几天里，我觉得很孤独，直到有一天早晨当我正沿公路走时，一个刚到村里的男子叫住了我。

　　"到西卵村该怎么走?"他很疲倦地问我。

　　我告诉了他。知道自己不是这个镇里最近才来的人，我很高兴，我现在成了向导。我走回家时，阳光普照，绿树成荫，我感到生命随着夏天一起复苏了。

　　那年夏天我读了很多书，也买了许多关于银行和金融方面的书。所有的书都摆在书架上，看来都很重要，保准能给我讲述致富的诀窍，我打算把这些书都读完。上大学时我对文学很感兴趣，因此现在我计划用伟大的文学和其他娱乐活动来充实我的生活。

go rented 这里的go具有连系动词的性质。表示"处于某种状态"，后跟过去分词或形容词。本处意为"继续租房子"。再如：His complaints went unnoticed. 他们的抱怨一直未引起注意。He often goes hungry.他经常挨饿。

some [sʌm] *adj.*修饰单数名词表示某个、某一。例如：Some person may object. 有人可能会反对。

修饰复数或不可数名词表示"若干、一些、一点、少量的"。例如：1. Some birds cannot fly. 有些鸟不会飞。2. Give me some work; I have nothing to do. 给我一点工作做吧，我现在没事干。

还常用于疑问句中，期待肯定答复或表示邀请、请求、劝导等；表示一些、一点、什么。例如：1. Can I have some milk, please? 请问我可以喝点牛奶吗？2. Would you like some wine? 你要喝点酒吗？

newest *adj.*是new的最高级形式。本处意为"最后到这里的"。

and now I planned to fill my days with great literature and other happy activities.

The house that I had rented was in one of the strangest places in the United States. It was on Long Island, New York State. The island was more than sixty miles long and just east of New York City. Between Long Island and the city was a narrow part of the Atlantic Ocean called Long Island Sound. On the ocean coast, twenty miles from New York City, there are two strange pieces of land, both of which look a lot like eggs. They are called West Egg and East Egg and a small bay flows between them. But although they are the same in shape and size they are also quite different in many ways.

I lived in West Egg, the cheaper, and certainly less nice, of the two eggs. My little house was near the sea, between two very huge houses. The one on my right side was very large and was a copy of some famous house in France. It had a swimming pool and a huge garden that would take an hour to walk around. I knew that a rich gentleman named Mr. Gatsby lived there. My house was small and ugly and looked very silly next to Gatsby's huge palace, but I could see the water from my house and I was happy.

It was nice to live so close to such rich people. I wanted to know their stories and their secrets. I thought that I might be one of them some day. And this feeling grew as I looked across the water at the expensive white houses of East Egg. They

我租的房子在美国最神奇的地方之一
——纽约州的长岛上。长岛正位于纽约市东
边，有六十多英里长。纽约市与长岛之间是大
西洋的一个狭窄的水域，叫长岛海峡。在离纽
约市二十英里远的海岸上有两块奇怪的陆地，
看起来都非常像鸡蛋，分别叫西卵镇和东卵
镇，二者中间有一个小海湾。尽管二者形状和
大小相同，但在许多方面它们却迥然相异。

我住在西卵镇，是两卵之中较便宜当然
也是不那么好的一个。我的小房子紧靠着海，
夹在两所大房子之间。我右边的那一幢房子很
大，是法国某些名宅的翻版。有一个游泳池，
还有一个大花园，绕一圈得花一个小时。我了
解到有个叫盖茨比先生的富有绅士住在那儿。
我的房子又小又丑，挨着盖茨比的巨大宫殿，
看起来很简陋。但从我的房子里能看到海水，
我就很高兴了。

住得离这样的富人这么近，真是妙极了。
我想了解他们的故事和秘密，想着总有一天我
或许会成为他们其中的一员。当我的目光越过
水面看着东卵镇那边那些昂贵的白房子时，这
种感觉就会增强。它们看起来几乎就像高耸在

7

looked almost like palaces standing high above the water.

The story of my summer really begins on the day I drove over to East Egg to have dinner with Tom and Daisy Buchanan. Daisy was my cousin, but not a *close* one. Tom attended the same university that I did. A few years after they got married I had spent two days with them in Chicago. Still, I didn't feel close to them.

In university Tom had been one of the strongest football players. He seemed to love the game and all of the people that watched him play.

Tom's family was extremely rich. After they left Chicago, they lived for a few years in France for no real reason. They then traveled to many places to live. Tom and Daisy both had horses and they would go anywhere that people rode horses and were rich together. I don't know why they came to the East. Daisy told me that they planned to stay in New York for a long time, but I didn't believe her. Tom would always want to move again and again, it was likely he was looking for the excitement of one of his past football games.

It was hard to understand that Tom, a man my same age, was rich enough to move around the world, *buying houses and riding horses*.

One warm night I went over to East Egg to see Tom and Daisy. I felt that I hardly knew them. Their house was even larger than I could see from West Egg. It was a large house

水面上的宫殿似的。

就从我驱车去东卵镇与汤姆和黛西·布坎南夫妇一块吃饭那天起，我那个夏天里的故事才真正开始。黛西是我的表妹，但关系并不近，汤姆和我同在一所大学上过学。他们结婚几年后，我在芝加哥与他们一块儿呆过两天，但我对他们仍然没有亲近的感觉。

汤姆曾是大学里最强壮的橄榄球运动员之一。他好像喜欢这项运动以及所有看他打球的人。

汤姆的家庭非常富裕。他们离开芝加哥之后，漫无目的地在法国住了几年，然后又到许多地方去住过。汤姆和黛西都有马，他们会到有人骑马和富人聚集的任何地方。我不知道他们为什么来到了东部，黛西告诉我他们打算在纽约呆很长时间，但我不相信。汤姆总是想一搬再搬，可能是在寻找过去参加某场橄榄球赛时的那种刺激。

真难以理解汤姆这个和我同龄的人如此富裕，足以周游世界、买房、骑马。

在一个温暖的夜晚，我去东卵镇看汤姆和黛西。我觉得几乎不认识他们了。他们的房子比我能在西卵镇看到的还要大得多。这是一

close [kləuz] *adj.* 密切的、亲密的，这里指近亲。feel close to sb. 感到与某人很近。
buying houses and riding horses 是现在分词短语，表示伴随状况，修饰动词 move，直译为"同时又能买房、买车"。

9

from the nineteenth-century. It was near the water and their garden began at the beach and came all the way up to the front door. The front of the house was full of tall windows; all the windows were open now to let the warm summer winds come in.

Tom Buchanan was standing at the front door wearing his horse-riding clothes. He looked the same as he did during university. He was still a strong man and, like me, was about thirty years old. His mouth was *hard-looking* and his face looked like he was scolding someone. His horse-riding clothes could not hide the great strength of his body. His body was a body full of power — a cruel body.

The sound of his voice was rough and made him seem even more scolding. When we were in university, many men hated him. We were never close friends, but I always thought that he liked me and hoped that I liked him also.

I walked up to greet him and we talked for a while.

"I've got a nice house here," he said as he *grasped* my arm and turned my body around. He pointed his wide and fat finger at the garden, the roses and the boat sitting on the beach.

" I bought this house from the rich oil man, Mr. Demaine." He turned me around again suddenly and declared, "We'll go inside now."

We walked through a high hall and went into a bright

幢19世纪的大房子，靠着海，花园从海边一直延伸到前门。房子前一部分全是高大的窗子，现在所有的窗子都开着，好让夏日的暖风吹进来。

汤姆·布坎南穿着一身骑装站在前门，看起来和在大学时一样。他仍很强壮，像我一样大约三十岁。他的嘴看上去很冷酷，从脸色上看，他好像正在骂人。他那身骑装隐藏不住他身体内巨大的力量，他的身体充满了能量——一个冷酷无情的躯体。

他说话的声音很粗鲁，这使得他更像是在骂人。上大学时，许多人都恨他。我俩从来都不是亲密的朋友，但我一直认为他喜欢我，并且希望我也喜欢他。

我走过去向他问好，然后就聊了一会儿。他抓住我的胳膊，把我转过来说："我在这儿买了一处漂亮的房子。"他粗壮的手指指着花园、玫瑰花和停在海滩上的小船。

"我从石油富商德梅因先生那儿买了这套房子。"他突然又把我转过来说，"现在我们就进去看看。"

我们穿过一个高高的大厅，走进一间明

hard-looking 看上去冷酷无情的，不友好的

grasp [grɑːsp] *vt.*抓住。此词的选用体现了汤姆的傲慢、鲁莽的性格。请注意小说中多处用了这类动词刻画汤姆这一人物性格特点。

room. There were long windows on both sides. The windows were open and white sunlight was coming in *as well as* the smell of fresh grass. A wind blew through the room.

A huge sofa was in the room and two young women were sitting on it. They were both wearing white and their dresses were moving in the wind. It looked like they had just been blown into the room by the wind after flying around the house. I stood there for a minute listening to the wind. Then Tom closed the windows, and the two young women's dresses stopped moving.

One of the women was my cousin, Daisy; the other woman was younger and was a stranger to me. She was lying on the sofa and she didn't move at all when I came in. She didn't even move her head to look up and see who had come in the room.

Daisy tried to stand up, but was sitting too deeply in the sofa. She laughed a little laugh and I laughed too and walked towards her into the room.

"I'm so happy to see you," she said. She then laughed again, as if she had said something very funny, and held my hand in her hands. She looked into my eyes, as if there was no other person in the world she wanted to see as much as me. That was the special character that Daisy had. She made everybody feel very special and important. She whispered in my ear that the name of the other girl was Miss Baker.

Now Miss Baker's mouth opened a little and she turned

亮的房子。房子两面都是落地长窗，窗子开着，小草清新的气息飘进来白花花的阳光洒进来，一阵风儿吹过整个房间。

屋里有张大沙发，上面正坐着两个年轻女人，她们都身着白裙，裙子正随风飘动，好像她们绕房子飘飞之后刚刚被风吹进屋子。我站在那儿，听了一会儿风声。然后汤姆关上了窗子，两个年轻女人的裙子也随之停止了飘动。

其中一个女子是我的表妹黛西；另一个更年轻，我不认识。我进来时，她躺在沙发上丝毫没动，甚至也没抬头看看是谁进来了。

黛西想站起来，但她在沙发里陷得太深了。她笑了笑，我也笑了笑，就冲她走进了屋子。

"很高兴见到你。"她说着又笑了一下，好像刚说了什么特别滑稽的话。她握住我的手，看着我的眼睛，好像我是世界上她惟一最想见的人。这就是黛西性格的独特之处，她使每个人都感觉自己很特别很重要。她悄悄地对我耳语道另外那个女孩是贝克小姐。

这时贝克小姐的嘴微微张了一下，并朝

as well as 1. 除…之外还（也、和），例如：(1) Hiking is good exercise as well as fun. (也) 长途散步既是好的锻炼方法，也很有趣。(2) In theory as well as in practice, the idea is unsound. (和) 无论在理论上还是在实践上，这种想法都不令人满意。2. 与…一样（程度），例如：He would like to go as well as you. 和你一样，他也愿意去。

her head a little toward me. Her eyes didn't show any feelings, good or bad.

My cousin began to ask me questions about my recent life and work. She spoke in a low and exciting voice. Her face was beautiful, but also sad. Her eyes were bright and her voices made you feel safe. Most men could not forget her after they saw her even once.

I told her that I had visited Chicago when coming to New York, and that many people there asked me to wish her happy days.

"Do they miss me?" she cried happily.

"All of Chicago is sad that you have left. The whole city wears black clothing to show their sadness."

"How wonderful! Let's go back, Tom. Tomorrow!" Then she said to me, "You should see our baby."

"Can I see her now?" I asked.

"She's *asleep* right now. She's three years old. Haven't you ever seen her?"

"Never."

"Well. You should see her. She's — "

Tom Buchanan, who had been nervously walking in a circle around the room, stopped and put his hand on my shoulder.

"What are you doing for work now, Nick?"

"I sell bonds."

"Whom do you work for?"

我稍微抬了抬头。她的眼里没有流露出任何神情，不管是善意的还是恶意的。

表妹问了我最近生活和工作方面的一些问题。她的声音很小，但很兴奋。她的脸长得很漂亮，但同时神情也很忧伤。她的眼睛很明亮，她的声音使你感到很安全，大多数男人哪怕只见她一次都忘不了。

我告诉她，我来纽约时又去了趟芝加哥，那儿的许多人要我代他们祝她幸福。

"他们想我吗？"她快活地大声说道。
"你走了，芝加哥所有的人都很难过，整个城市的人都穿着黑衣服表示他们的悲伤。"
"太好了！我们回去吧，汤姆。明天就走！"然后她对我说："你应该看看我们的小宝宝。"

"现在可以吗？"我问。
"她正睡着呢。她三岁了。你从没见过她吧？"

"从来没有。"
"那，你应该看看她。她是……"

本来一直在屋子里不安地转来转去的汤姆·布坎南停下来，把手放到我肩上。
"尼克，你现在做什么工作？"
"我在卖债券。"
"为哪家公司工作？"

asleep [əˈsliːp] *adj.*[表语] 睡着的，再如：He was asleep with his head on his arms. 他头枕着胳膊睡着了。有时表示（四肢）麻木的，例如：My foot is asleep, probably because I've been lying on it. 我的脚麻了，可能是因为我一直压着的事儿。

adv. 用于 fall / drop asleep，表示睡着了，进入睡眠状态。例如：One after another, all three of them fell asleep. 一个接一个，他们三个都睡着了。

I told him.

"I've never *heard of* them," he said very seriously.

This annoyed me. "You will hear of them soon," I answered.

Suddenly Miss Baker stood up. "I'm tired," she cried. "I've been *lying* on that sofa all day."

"Don't blame me," Daisy said. "I've been trying to go to New York with you all afternoon."

A helper brought in four glasses of wine, and offered them to us.

"No, thanks," said Miss Baker. "I'm training for a big golf match."

Tom looked at her shocked. "You're training?" He drank his wine as if it were only a drop in the bottom of the glass.

I looked at Miss Baker and saw that she was quite pretty. Her gray eyes looked back at me now with interest and politeness. Her face was pale and lovely. I realized now that I had seen her, or a picture of her, before.

"You live in West Egg," she said. "I have a friend there."

"I don't know any people in — " I began to say.

" — you must know Mr. Gatsby."

Before I could tell Miss Baker that Gatsby was my neighbor, the helper came into the room and told us that dinner was

我告诉了他。

"我从来没听说过他们。"他非常严肃地说。

这话让我心里很不舒服。"你很快会听说他们的。"我回答道。

贝克小姐突然站了起来。"我烦死了,"她大声说道。"我已经在沙发上躺一整天了。"

"不要怪我。"黛西说。"我整个下午一直劝你跟我一块去纽约。"

一个用人拿过来四杯酒——递给我们。

"不,谢谢了。"贝克小姐说。"我在参加大型高尔夫比赛的训练。"

汤姆吃惊地看着她。"你在训练?"他一口喝完酒,好像只有一滴酒在杯底似的。

我看了看贝克小姐,发现她很漂亮。这时她的灰眼睛也正感兴趣而礼貌地看着我。她的面容苍白而动人,现在我意识到我以前曾见过她或她的照片。

"你住在西卵镇,"她说。"我那儿有个朋友。"

"在那儿我不认识任何人——"我开始说。

"——你一定认识盖茨比先生。"

我刚要告诉贝克小姐,盖茨比是我的邻居,用人就进来说晚餐准备好了。汤姆又抓住

hear of = hear about 听到有关…的消息,听说,得知。例如:She hasn't heard about /of her husband's death. 她还没有听到她丈夫去世的消息。还可表示"知道、知道有"。例如:I have never heard of the city. 我从来不知道有那座城市。

lying ['laiiŋ] 是不及物动词lie的现在分词,意为"平卧、躺着",例如:He is lying on his side. 他正侧身躺着。另外,lie还有"说谎、欺骗"的意思。例如:You are lying. 你在说谎。

注意:表示"躺着"这一意思时,是不规则动词,其过去式和过去分词分别是lay, lain。不要和表示"说谎"的动词lie(规则动词,过去式是lied,过去分词是lied)相混淆。

17

ready. Tom again grasped my arm and moved me into the garden. The two young women were in front of us and they sat down *at a table* that had been put out there. The wind had stopped and there were four candles burning on the table.

"Why use candles?" said Daisy as she blew them out. "In two weeks it will be the longest day of the year." She looked around at each of us brightly. "I always wait for the longest day of the year and then miss it. Do you always wait for it and then miss it?"

Nobody answered her question.

"We should plan something to do," said Miss Baker in a tired voice. She was sitting at the table as if she were getting into bed. She turned toward Daisy, and then she and Daisy talked together. Their conversation was just chat and had no meaning. They sat there chatting, and they didn't *pay* much *attention to* Tom and me. They were polite, but they knew that soon our dinner would end, and then everyone would go home and go to sleep and that nobody would care or remember any of it. It was very different from my home in the Midwest, where an evening was full of activities and talking.

The telephone then rang inside the house and the helper went to answer it. He came back and whispered something into Tom's ear. Tom's face looked very annoyed, and he went inside without saying a word to any of us.

Daisy moved her head towards me and said, "I'm so hap-

我的胳膊，把我拉进花园。两个年轻女子走在前面，坐在早已摆在那儿的桌子边。风停了，桌子上燃着四支蜡烛。

"干嘛点蜡烛？"黛西说着就把它们吹灭了。"两周以后就是一年里最长的一天了。"她高兴地环视着我们每一个人。"我总是在等一年里最长的一天，临了还是错过了。你们是不是也有一直在等，临了也还是错过了的时候呢？

没有人回答她。

"我们应该计划做点什么，"贝克小姐懒懒地说。她坐在桌边，就好像要上床睡觉似的。她转向黛西，于是二人聊了起来。她们只是闲聊，没什么实际意义。她们坐那儿聊着，并不在意汤姆和我。她们很礼貌，但她们知道晚餐很快就会结束，然后每个人都会回家睡觉，没有人会在意或记住这一切。这跟我在中西部的家里很不一样，那里晚上会有许多活动和交谈。

这时屋里的电话响了，用人过去接电话。他回来后，对汤姆耳语了几句。汤姆的脸色看起来很难看，他没跟我们任何人说一个字就走进屋里。

黛西把头转向我说，"你今晚能来这儿，

at a table 在桌旁。注意at table 引申为"进餐"的意思。
pay attention to 注意、关注某人。注意pay one's attentions to 则意为"殷勤款待某人、向（女人）献殷勤"。

py that you could come here tonight. I love to see you in my home, Nick. You are like — like a rose."

This was not true. I am not like a rose, not even a little bit like a rose. She was only saying the first thing that she could think of — but still a warm feeling came from her exciting voice. The words that she said did not seem important, only her voice was important. Then suddenly Daisy stood up and went into the house.

Miss Baker and I looked at each other for a moment. I opened my mouth and was going to speak, but Miss Baker put her finger next to her mouth and said "Shhhhhhh!" Sitting at the table we could hear Tom's voice talking on the telephone inside. I *tried* to hear what he was saying, but I couldn't hear clearly. Miss Baker moved her ear closer, trying to hear him, but his voice stopped.

I began to talk again, "You said that you know Mr. Gatsby. He is my neighbor — "

Again, Miss Baker put her finger up to her mouth. "Shhhhhhhh! Don't talk. I want to hear what happens."

"Is something important happening inside?" I asked.

"You really don't know?" said Miss Baker. "I thought that everybody in East and West Egg knew."

"I don't."

"Why — Tom's another woman — some secret woman in New York."

我很高兴。尼克，我喜欢在我家里看到你。你
像——像一朵玫瑰。"

这根本不对。我不像玫瑰，一点儿也不
像玫瑰。她只是脑子里一想到什么就说出
来——不过，从她那兴奋的声音里仍能感觉到
一股热情。她说的话似乎并不重要，重要的只
是她的声音。接着黛西突然站起来，走进屋
里。

贝克小姐和我对视了一会儿。我口正
要说话，但贝克小姐把手指放到嘴边说：
"嘘——！"坐在桌边我们能听到屋里汤姆
打电话的声音。我试图想听他在说些什
么，但听不清楚。贝克小姐把耳朵移近
点，也想听到，可是他的声音停住了。

我又开始说话了，"你说你认识盖茨比
先生，他是我的邻居——"

贝克小姐又把手指放到嘴上。"嘘——！
别说话。我想听听发生了什么事。"

"里面发生什么重要的事了吗？"我问。

"你真不知道？"贝克小姐说。"我以为
东卵镇和西卵镇的所有人都知道了。"

"我不知道。"

"嗯——汤姆的另一个女人——在纽约的
某个秘密的女人。"

try [trai] v.尝试、试图。try
后接不定式和动名词时意义不
同：接不定式可表示"一种尝
试，但不一定成功"。He tried
to run, but he soon tired. 他试
图奔跑，但很快就累了。（没
成功）接动名词可表示"尝
试，并做到了"。My friend
tried running five miles a day.
我的朋友每天都尝试着跑五英
里。（做到了）

21

"Another woman?" I repeated stupidly.

"Yes. It was very stupid for her to telephone him during dinner, though. Daisy is around."

Before I could ask her more questions, Tom and Daisy returned to the table. I tried not to look at their eyes.

A few minutes later we all stood up from the table. The helpers quickly came and cleaned up the glasses and plates. Tom and Miss Baker went inside and I walked with Daisy into the garden.

Daisy looked out at the sea and the sun slowly moved down.

"We don't know each other very well, Nick," she said. "We are cousins, but you didn't even come to my wedding."

"I was still in Europe fighting in the war." I told her.

"Oh, yes. That's true." She paused and thought for a while. "Well, my life has not been good, Nick. Now I'm feeling that there is no hope in this world for me."

Obviously she had a good reason to be. I knew about Tom's other woman and she did too. I listened silently, but Daisy *stopped* speaking. I began to ask her questions about her baby daughter.

"Is she talking yet, and — eating, and — walking?"

"Oh, yes." She looked at me. "Listen, Nick, let me tell you what I said the day when she was born. Would you like to know?"

"另一个女人？"我傻乎乎地重复着。

"对，不过，她晚饭时打电话给他也太傻了。黛西在旁边呢。"

没等我再问，汤姆和黛西就回到桌边了。我尽量不与他们对视。

几分钟后，我们都从桌边站起来。佣人很快走过来收拾杯盘。汤姆和贝克小姐走进屋里，我和黛西则走进花园。

黛西眺望着大海，此时太阳正缓缓下落。

"尼克，我们彼此不太熟悉，"她说。"我们是表兄妹，但是你连我的婚礼都没有参加。"

"我那时还在欧洲打仗。"我告诉她。

"噢，对。的确如此。"她停下来，想了一会儿。"咳，我过得并不好，尼克。现在我感觉对于我来说这个世界已经没有希望了。"

显然她有充分的理由。我知道汤姆有另一个女人，她也知道。我静静地听着，但黛西停了下来不说了。我开始问起她的宝贝女儿。

"她会说话了吗，还有——会吃东西，——会走路了吗？"

"噢，会。"她看着我。"听着，尼克，我来告诉你她出生那天我说的话。你想知道吗？"

stop [stɔp] ***vt.*** 接动名词表示"停止、使中断、使停下"正在做的事。I couldn't stop laughing at the joke. 听了这个笑话，我情不自禁地笑个没完。

vi. 接动词不定式表示"停止、中断、突然停下"去做另一件事。例如：They stopped to say hello. 他们停下来打招呼。

it [it] ***pron.*** 用于指婴孩。it通常指无生命物、动物、植物，在性别忽略或不详时也指人或婴孩。

23

"Yes. Very much."

"It'll show you how I feel about — life. Well, I asked the nurse if the baby was a boy or a girl. When she told me that it was a girl, I turned my head away and cried. Then I said, 'I'm glad it's a girl. And I hope she'll be a stupid fool — that's the best thing a girl can be in this world, a beautiful little fool.'"

"I think that everything's just terrible," she went on. "Everybody thinks so — the smartest people think so. And I know that it is true. I've been all over the world and seen everything and done everything."

When she stopped talking, I felt nervous. I knew what she had said was not true. I waited silently and a moment later she looked at me with a proud smile on her lovely face. She proudly believed *that* she and Tom had traveled all around the world and *that* they were a part of this small group of people who knew a lot about the world.

We went back inside. Tom and Miss Baker were sitting on the long sofa, and she was reading the newspaper to him. When we came in she stopped reading and stood up.

"Ten o'clock," she said. "*It's time for* this good girl *to* go to bed."

"Jordan's going to play in the golf game tomorrow," explained Daisy, "over at Westchester Club."

"Oh Miss Baker — you must be Jordan Baker."

"想。非常想。"

"这会让你知道我是怎样感受——生活。唔，我问护士小宝宝是男孩还是女孩。当她告诉我是个女孩时，我转过头就哭了。然后我说，'我很高兴是个女孩。并且我希望她是个傻瓜——那是女孩子在这个世界上最好的出路了，一个漂亮的小傻瓜。'"

"我认为一切都很糟，"她接着说。"每个人都会这么想——最聪明的人也会这么想。而且我知道这是真的。我到过世界各地，什么都见过，什么都做过。"

她停下来不说了，我感到很紧张。我知道她说的不是实话。我静静地等着，过了一会儿，她看了看我，可爱的脸上带着自豪的微笑。她自豪地认为她和汤姆已经走遍了世界，他们是那个非常了解这个世界的小团体的一部分。

我们回到屋里。汤姆和贝克小姐正坐在长沙发上，她正在读报给他听。我们进来时她停下并站了起来。

"十点啦，"她说。"我这个乖女孩该睡觉了。"

"乔丹明天要参加高尔夫球赛，"黛西解释道，"在威斯彻斯特俱乐部那边。"

"噢，贝克小姐——你一定是乔丹·贝克。"

that [ðæt] *pron.* 句中的两个that从句是由believe引导的两个并列宾语从句。

it's time for sb. to do sth. 到了某人该做某事的时候了。it作虚主语（empty subject），常指时间、天气、温度和距离。再如：It's time for me to go home. 我该回家了。

25

I knew now why her face was so familiar — I had seen pictures of her in many photographs in many golf clubs, she was quite a famous golf player. I had even heard some people talking about her before. They were telling bad stories about her, but I could not remember what it was.

"Good night," she said. "Daisy, please wake me at eight." She then looked at me for a moment, "Good night, Mr. Carraway. See you soon." She went upstairs.

"Of course you will see each other," said Daisy. "I think I'll even arrange a marriage. Come over often, Nick, and I'll help bring you two together."

"She's a nice girl," said Tom after Miss Baker went upstairs. "They shouldn't let her travel around the country all *alone*."

"Who shouldn't let her?" asked Daisy in a cold voice.

"Her family."

"Her family only has one aunt, and she must be about a thousand years old. Anyway, Now Nick can take care of her. You will go out with her, won't you, Nick? She's going to spend lots of weekends at our house this summer."

"*Is* she *from* New York?" I asked.

"She's from my home town. We went to the same school and were young girls together."

I decided to go home and stood up. Daisy and Tom walked to the door with me and stood together watching me

我现在才知道为什么感到她这么面熟——我曾在许多高尔夫俱乐部的众多照片中见过她，她是一位颇有名气的高尔夫球手。我以前甚至还听人谈论过她，说她有什么不好的事儿，但我不记得是什么事了。

"晚安，"她说。"黛西，明早八点叫醒我。"然后她看了看我，"晚安，卡罗威先生。再见！"她上了楼。

"当然你们会再见面的，"黛西说。"我想我甚至会做个媒的。尼克，常来啊，我会帮你们撮合的。"

"她是个不错的姑娘，"贝克小姐上楼后汤姆说。"他们不该让她单独一个人在全国各地乱跑。"

"谁不该让她？"黛西冷冷地问。

"她家里。"

"她家里只有一个姑妈，而且她也一把年纪啦。无论如何，现在尼克可以照顾她了。尼克，你会跟她一块外出的，是吗？今年夏天她会在我家泡上很多个周末的。"

"她是纽约人吗？"我问。

"她是我同乡。我们在同一所学校上学，一块儿度过少女时期。"

我决定回家了，就站起来。黛西和汤姆送我走到门口，然后两人站在一起看着我朝汽

alone [ə'ləun] *adj.* 只作表语，表示"单独的、孤独的"。例如：1. She was alone in that dark room. 她独自一人呆在那黑屋子里。2. I felt very alone in the clearing. 在那林中空地，我感到十分孤独。用在本文中在名词或代词后面表示"只、只有、仅仅、单单"。例如：One boy alone can do this work. 只要一个男孩子就能做这工作了。

adv. 单独地、独自地、仅、只

be from = come from 是…地方的人

27

walk to my car. Before I drove away Daisy yelled,   "Wait! I forgot to ask you something. We heard you were going to get married."

"That's right," Tom agreed.   "We heard that you were preparing to marry a girl from West."

"It's not true." I yelled back, "I'm too poor."

"But we heard it," Daisy repeated.   "We heard it from three people, so it must be true."

I knew that they were talking about my old girlfriend in the Midwest. One of the reasons I had left the Midwest and came to the East was because so many people were saying I was going to marry my girlfriend. I didn't want to stop seeing my old girlfriend just because people were saying that we were getting married, but I also wasn't going to get married just because my family and friends were *putting* pressure on me.

Tom and Daisy's interest in my life made me feel special. But as I drove away I felt full of doubt about Daisy and Tom, and a little angry. It seemed to me that the only thing that Daisy could do in her situation was to run out of her house with her daughter in her arms.

When I arrived back at my house in West Egg I put the car in the garage and then sat for a while in the yard. The wind had stopped blowing, and the moon was bright. I watched a cat moving slowly across the moonlight, and, as I turned my head to watch it, I saw that a man had come out of my neighbor's

车走去。我刚要开车走，黛西大声喊："等等！我忘了问你点事。我们听说你要结婚了。"

"是的，"汤姆附和道。"我们听说你准备娶一个西部的姑娘。"

"没这事。"我大声回答道，"我太穷了。"

"但我们听说是的，"黛西重复道。"我们听三个人说过，因此这一定是真的。"

我知道他们说的是我原来在中西部时的那个女朋友。我离开中西部来到东部的原因之一就是许多人说我要和我的女朋友结婚了。我不想就因为人们在说我跟女朋友要结婚了而停止见她，但我也不打算迫于家人和朋友的压力而凑合着结婚。

汤姆和黛西如此关注我的生活让我感到很特别。但是我开车离开的时候，对黛西和汤姆充满了疑问，也有点生气。依我看，处在这种境况下，黛西惟一能做的就是抱着她的女儿逃出这幢房子。

我回到西卵镇的家后，把车停到车库里，然后在院子里坐了一会儿。风停了，月色皎洁。我看见一只猫在月光下慢慢地走着，正当我扭头看时，一个男子从邻居家的房子里走了出来。他双手插在衣兜里，站在那儿仰望星星。我想他也许就是盖茨比先生，但黑暗中我

put + obj. 迫使承担…

house. He was standing with his hands in his pockets and looking up at the stars. I thought that maybe he was Mr. Gatsby, but I could not see him clearly in the darkness.

I decided to yell to the man. Miss Baker had talked about Gatsby at dinner, and I could use that as an introduction. But I decided not to yell to him, because I suddenly felt that he wanted to be alone. He moved his arms towards the sea. I looked towards the water also, and could not see anything except a small green light. The light was very small and very far away; it was on the coast of East Egg. I looked at the light for a moment and when I again looked for Gatsby he had left. Again I was alone in the night.

看不清他。

　　我决定朝那人喊一声。吃饭时贝克小姐谈到盖茨比，我可以借此来做个自我介绍。但我又决定不朝他喊了，因为我突然感觉他想单独呆会儿。他双臂伸向大海，我也朝海上望去，除了一点绿光之外，什么也没看见。那光亮很小也很远，是在东卵镇的海边上。我朝那光亮看了一会儿，等我再看见盖茨比时，他已经离开了。黑暗之中又剩我一个人了。

CHAPTER TWO Tom's Other Woman

T he Long Island railroad comes from New York City to West Egg. When driving by car from West Egg into the city, the road joins the railroad tracks and follows next to it for a short way. The train stops at this place. This area is very dirty and piles of earth sit on either side of the road. Clouds of dirt always cover this gray place. Dirty workmen are there everyday working with tools on these piles of dirt.

Behind the largest pile of dirt is a large sign. The sign has a picture of a man named Doctor T.J. Eckleburg. His eyes are huge, large and yellow and they look like they are looking down at all the cars driving by. The eyes of Doctor T.J. Eckleburg seem not to be on his face, but, instead, they are on a pair of wide yellow glasses. I guess that Dr. Eckleburg *moved away from* this dirty area, but left his advertisement here.

It was here that I met Tom Buchanan's "other woman" for the first time.

I was interested to see this woman, just to know what she looked like, but I didn't have any desire to meet her. I did meet her though. I was taking the train with Tom into New York and when we got to the piles of dirt he stood up and said that he wanted to *get off* the train for a bit. I asked him why and he said, "I want you to meet my girl." He then grasped my arm and pulled me out of the train.

第二章 汤姆的另一个女人

长岛铁路从纽约市一直通到西卵镇。开车从西卵镇进入市区,公路与铁路相交后又在它旁边延伸了一小段路,这就是火车停车站。这一带非常脏,路两边全是土堆。大团大团的尘土总是笼罩着这片灰地。满身灰尘的工人们手持工具每天都在这些灰堆上劳作。

在最大的一个灰堆后有一个大标牌,标牌上有T·J·埃克尔堡医生的画像。他空洞的双眼又大又黄,看上去像在俯视着经过的所有汽车。这双眼睛好像不在他的脸上,倒像是在一幅宽大的黄色眼镜上。我猜埃克尔堡医生一定是从这个脏兮兮的地区搬走了,可他的广告牌还留在这儿。

我就是在这儿第一次见到汤姆·布坎南的"另一个女人"的。

我对见这个女人有兴趣只是想知道她长得怎么样,但我并不巴望着跟她会面。不过我还是见到她了。我和汤姆坐火车去纽约,走到这些灰堆边时,他起身说他想下火车办点儿小事。我问他办什么事,他说:"我想叫你认识我的女朋友。"然后他拽住我的胳膊把我拉下了火车。

move away from = move off 离开

get off = get out of 下车、离开

33

Everyone knew that Tom had a second woman. His friends did not agree with the way he brought her with him to popular restaurants, as if he wanted to *show* her *off* to the world. They all thought that it was a big risk and that it would hurt Daisy's feelings.

Tom and I walked along the dirty road; Doctor Eckleburg's eyes seemed to watch us. The only building I could see was a small yellow one made out of brick. It was standing alone in the empty land. The building had three stores inside, one of them was a café, and I could see lines of dirt leading to the door, the next store was empty; the last store was a garage to fix cars — GEORGE B. WILSON'S CAR REPAIRS, said the sign in front.

Tom and I went into the garage. It was empty and dirty inside. There was only one car inside; it was old and covered with dust. Mr. Wilson came out of the door of his office. He was a sad-looking man with a pale face. *It looked like* he was a handsome man when he was young, but now he just looked old and tired. *It seemed that* he had lost all of his spirit for life.

"Hey, Wilson," said Tom. "How's business?"

"Not too bad," said Wilson unhappily. "When are you going to sell me your old car?"

"Soon — maybe next week; I'm fixing it right now."

Tom's eyes were jumping up and down and looking nervously around the garage. A moment later a woman with a

每个人都知道汤姆还有个女人。他的朋友们不同意他把她带到人多的饭馆的做法，他好像要把她向公众显示似的。他们都认为这太冒险，会伤害黛西的感情。

我和汤姆沿着脏脏的路走着；埃克尔堡医生的眼睛好像在注视着我们。我能看到的惟一建筑是砖砌的小黄屋子，孤零零地立在空地中。黄屋子里有三个隔间，第一间是咖啡间，我能看到一条条灰印儿直通到门口；第二间是空的；最后一间是汽车修理行，门前的牌子上写着——乔治·B·威尔逊汽车修理铺。

我和汤姆走进车行。里面又空又脏，只有一辆车停在那儿，车很旧，上面布满灰尘。威尔逊先生从办公室里走出来，他面色苍白，神情忧郁。他年轻时像是很英俊，可如今他显得又老又累，好像已经失去了对生活的全部激情。

"嗨，威尔逊，"汤姆说。"生意怎么样？"

"还不算太坏，"威尔逊不快地说。"你打算什么时候把你的旧汽车卖给我？"

"快了——也许是下周吧；我正在修它呢。"

汤姆的眼睛忽上忽下焦急地扫视着整个车行。过了一会儿一个周身浑圆的女人从办公

show off 显示优点。Gold frame shows off the picture nicely. 金边使画看起来很漂亮。

it + look like + clause = to be probable that 可能是

It + seems/seemed + (that) clause 表示 "看起来好像…"

round body came out of the office door. She looked like she
was between thirty and forty years old, and was *rather* fat. Her
face and body were not beautiful, but she seemed to have the
spirit of a wild animal and it made her seem strangely good-
looking.

She came into the room and walked past her husband like
he was not even there. She then smiled slowly at Tom and
shook his hand.

"Get some chairs, so our guests can sit down," Mrs. Wilson said to her husband, who ran into the office.

"I want to see you," said Tom. "Get on the next train to
the city."

"Okay." She whispered.

"I'll meet you at the train station."

She quickly moved away from Tom and just at that moment George Wilson came out of the office with two chairs.

We left the garage and walked to the train station and
then waited for Mrs. Wilson.

"It's a dirty and terrible place, isn't it?" said Tom. "It's
good for her to get out of here sometime. I rent an apartment in
the city where we go sometimes."

"Doesn't her husband get angry that she goes into the city
all night?"

"Wilson is *so* stupid *that* he will never know. He thinks
that she is going into the city to see her sister."

室里走了出来。她看上去三四十岁，很胖。她的脸蛋和身材都不漂亮，但看上去有股野性，这使得她似乎有些奇怪地好看。

她走进屋子，从她丈夫身边走过，好像他根本不在那儿似的，继续朝汤姆慢悠悠地笑着，握了握他的手。

威尔逊太太对丈夫说："拿几把椅子来，给客人们坐。"他丈夫跑进办公室。

"我想见你，"汤姆说。"坐下一班火车去城里吧。"

"好的。"她低声说。

"我会在车站接你。"

她迅速从汤姆身边走开，就在这时乔治·威尔逊拿着两把椅子从办公室里走出来。

我们离开车行，走到火车站，然后等着威尔逊太太。

"这真是个又脏又糟糕的地方，是不是?"汤姆说。"她最好什么时候离开这里。我在市里租了套公寓，有时候我们在那儿约会。"

"她整夜都呆在城里，她丈夫不生气吗?"

"威尔逊太傻，他永远也不会知道。他会以为她要去市里看她的妹妹。

So I went together with Tom Buchanan and his girlfriend to New York. Mrs. Wilson sat in another train car *so that* no people would see her and Tom together.

Tom bought her a magazine and some soap with a heavy smell at the train station. Once in New York we got off the train and got into a taxi. She often stopped the taxi and made Tom buy her things.

"I want a dog," she said. The taxi stopped beside an old man with a basket full of very young dogs, which he was selling. "I want to get a dog for our apartment. They're nice to have — a dog."

"What kind are you selling?" asked Mrs. Wilson.

"Many kinds. What kind do you want, lady?"

"I want a police dog, the white ones with black spots; do you have that kind?"

The man looked with doubt into the basket and *pulled up* one of the animals *by the back of the neck.*

"That's not a police dog," said Tom.

"No, it's not exactly a police dog," said the man.

"I think it's sweet," said Mrs. Wilson. "How much is it?"

The man looked at the dog with great respect. "That dog will cost you ten dollars."

"Is it a boy or a girl?" she asked softly.

"*That dog*? That dog's a boy."

于是我跟汤姆·布坎南和他的女友一块儿去了纽约。威尔逊太太坐在另一节车厢里，这样就没人看见她和汤姆在一起了。

在火车站汤姆给她买了一本杂志和几块气味很浓的香皂。一到纽约，我们就下了火车，钻进出租车里，一路上她不时叫出租车停下，让汤姆给她买东西。

她说："我想要一只狗。"出租车在一个正拿着满满一篮子狗崽兜售的老人跟前停了下来。"我想给我们的公寓买只狗。养着挺可爱的——只要一只。"

"你卖的狗是什么品种的？"威尔逊太太问。

"有好多品种呢。太太，你想要哪一种？"

"我要一只警犬，带黑斑的白狗；你有这个品种的吗？"

那个老人迟疑地往篮子里看了看，然后抓着一只狗的后脖颈把它拽了出来。

"这不是警犬，"汤姆说。

"对，这确实不是警犬，"老人说。

"我觉得这个很可爱，"威尔逊太太说。"多少钱？"

老人带着赞赏的神情看着这只狗说："这条狗您要付10美元。"

"是公崽还是母崽？"她轻声问。

"这狗吗？是公崽。"

so that = in order that 为了、以便、使得。引导目的状语从句，例如：They are climbing higher so that they may get a better view. 他们爬得更高以便于看得更远。

pull up by the back of the neck 抓着后脖颈拎起。pull up, 抓起、拎起、拉起。by the back of the neck，by之后接人或物的某一部位时常用the。例如：I caught him by the shoulder. 我抓住了他的肩膀。

That dog? 这里暗含讽刺意味。本来是谈论狗，威尔逊太太却问它是 "boy" 还是 "girl"，以致于买狗人有点听不懂，才问了这句话。

"It's a girl," said Tom firmly. "Here's your money. Go and buy ten more dogs with it."

Mrs. Wilson picked up the dog and smiled happily. We then drove to the Fifth Avenue. I wanted to get out of the car and walk around the city, but they both insisted that I join them.

"I'll call my sister Catherine," said Mrs. Wilson, "and Mr. and Mrs. McKee from the apartment below."

Their apartment was at the top of a building on the 158th Street. Mrs. Wilson opened the door proudly and let me walk in first. The small living room was filled with expensive furniture that was much too large for it.

Mrs. Wilson gave the elevator boy some money and told him to go buy some milk, dog food and a box for the dog. Tom then brought out a bottle of strong wine and opened it.

Mrs. Wilson sat on Tom's knee and called her sister and the McKees on the telephone. I wanted a cigarette, but there were none in the house. I went out to buy some at the store on the corner. When I came back to the apartment both Tom and Mrs. Wilson had disappeared. I sat down in the living room and waited for them. About twenty minutes later they came out of the bedroom, just before Mrs. Wilson's sister arrived.

I don't drink much. In fact I have only been drunk twice in my whole life. That night was the second time. My memory of most of the conversation was not very clear. I remember that

"是母崽，"汤姆肯定地说。"给你钱。用它再多买十条狗吧。"

威尔逊太太接过狗，幸福地笑了。然后我们开到了第五街。我想下车在城里走走，但是他们坚持要我跟他们在一块儿。

"我要给我妹妹凯瑟琳打个电话，"威尔逊太太说，"还有下面公寓里的麦基先生和他太太。"

他们的公寓套间是在一五八街一幢楼的顶层。威尔逊太太趾高气扬地开了门，让我先进去。小小的客厅里摆满了大得很不相称的贵重家具。

威尔逊太太给电梯服务生一些钱，让他去买些牛奶、狗食和一个装狗的盒子。然后汤姆拿出一瓶烈酒并启开瓶塞。

威尔逊太太坐在汤姆膝盖上给她妹妹和麦基夫妇打电话。我想抽支烟，可屋子里没有。我出去在街角的商店里买了一点。我回到公寓时，汤姆和威尔逊太太两人都不见了。我坐在客厅里等他们，大约二十分钟后他们从卧室里出来，正好赶在威尔逊太太的妹妹到达之前。

我喝酒不多。事实上我一生中只喝醉过两次，那晚是第二次。大部分的谈话内容在我的记忆中都不太清楚了。我记得麦基太太的声

Mrs. McKee was loud and annoying and that her husband did-
n't speak much. I also remember that Mrs. Wilson's sister,
Catherine, was about thirty and attractive. She lived in the city
and knew much more about the world than Mrs. Wilson. She
sat down beside me on the sofa.

"Do you live near Tom?" she asked.

"I live in West Egg."

"Really? I was *down* in West Egg at a party about a
month ago. It was at the house of a man named Gatsby. Do you
know him?"

"He is my neighbor."

"People say that he is the nephew of the King of Germany. That's why he is so rich."

"Really?" I didn't think that this was true.

Catherine was staring at Tom and Mrs. Wilson. "My sister looks good with Tom, doesn't she?" She came close to me
and whispered in my ear, "You must know that they both
hate the people they're married to. They should get divorced
and then marry each other!"

I just sat there and didn't say anything, but she continued
talking, "Tom's wife is stopping them from getting a divorce.
She's a Catholic, and Catholic's don't believe in divorce."

I knew that Daisy was not a Catholic, and I immediately
understood that Tom had lied to Mrs. Wilson because he did
not want to marry her. I was a little shocked at Tom's lie.

音很大很烦而她丈夫却说话不多。我还记得威尔逊太太的妹妹凯瑟琳大约三十岁，长得很迷人。她住在市里，比威尔逊太太更懂人情世故。她挨着我坐在沙发上。

"你和汤姆住得近吗?" 她问。

"我住在西卵镇。"

"真的吗?大约一个月前我去西卵镇参加了一个聚会。是在一个叫盖茨比的人家里。你认识他吗?"

"他是我邻居。"

"人们说他是德国国王的侄子，所以他才这么富有。"

"真的吗?" 我想这不是真的。

凯瑟琳盯着汤姆和威尔逊太太。"我姐姐看上去和汤姆很般配，不是吗?" 她靠近我在我耳边低声说: "你一定知道他们都讨厌自己的那口子，他们应该离婚，然后再结婚!"

我只是坐在那儿，一句话都没说，但她还是不停地说: "汤姆的妻子不愿离婚，她是个天主教徒，天主教义不赞成离婚。"

我知道黛西不是天主教徒，我立即明白了汤姆对威尔逊太太撒了谎，因为他并不想娶她。我对汤姆撒的谎有点吃惊。

down [daun] *adv*.用作副词，有 "向下" 的意思。这里指从东卵镇到西卵镇。

43

As the evening continued we all finished the first bottle of strong wine and then a second one. Tom then gave the elevator boy some money to go out and buy some sandwiches, which were so big that they were a full dinner.

I wanted to leave the apartment and walk in the moonlight toward the park, but each time I tried to stand up Tom *would* grasp my arm and pull me back down.

Mrs. Wilson came over and sat next to me and she suddenly began to tell me the story of her first meeting with Tom.

"I was on the train to New York, I was coming here to see my sister, and he was sitting in front of me. He was wearing a nice suit and a clean, white shirt, and I couldn't stop looking at him. I was embarrassed though and I had to pretend that I was looking at the advertisement over his head. We began to talk and he was so brave. By the time that we arrived at the train station he was sitting next to me, and his body was close to mine. I told him I'd have to call a policeman if he sat any closer, but he knew I was kidding. When I got into a taxi with him I was so excited, in my head I thought, 'You can't live forever, you can't live forever.'"

I looked at my watch and it was nine o'clock. After what felt like only a few minutes I looked at my watch again and saw that it was already ten-thirty.

The little dog jumped up on the table and looked at Tom and Mrs. Wilson through the smoke of all the cigarettes. Tom

晚餐在继续，我们大家喝完一瓶烈性酒后又喝第二瓶。然后汤姆给电梯服务员一些钱让他出去买了些三明治，三明治很大，抵得上一顿完整的晚餐了。

我想离开公寓趁着月光朝公园的方向走走，但我每次想站起来，汤姆都抓住我的胳膊拉着我又坐回去。

威尔逊太太走过来坐在我旁边，突然她开始告诉我她和汤姆第一次见面的故事来。

"我坐火车到纽约来看我妹妹，他正坐在我前面。他穿着讲究的套装和一件洁白的衬衣，我禁不住地看他，却又很难为情，只好假装在看他头顶上的广告。我们开始谈话，他很大胆，火车到站时，他就坐在我旁边，他的身子紧紧挨着我的身子。我告诉他如果他再坐近些，我就叫警察，但他知道我是在开玩笑。当我和他坐进出租车里时，我很兴奋，脑子里在想：'人不能永远活下去，人不能永远活下去。'"

我看看表，九点了。感觉只过了一会儿后我又看表，发现已经十点半了。

小狗跳到桌子上，透过重重烟雾看着汤姆和威尔逊太太。汤姆和威尔逊太太正为什么

would [wud] *v.* 表示习惯行为。意为"每次我试着站起来，他都要……"

45

and Mrs. Wilson were fighting about something. It seemed as if Tom was telling Mrs. Wilson that she didn't have any right to speak about Daisy.

"Daisy! Daisy! Daisy!" shouted Mrs. Wilson. "I'll say her name whenever I want to! Daisy! Daisy! Dai — "

Tom made a short and fast move with his fist and broke Mrs. Wilson's nosc. Suddenly there was blood everywhere and everyone began to yell. Catherine ran to get some ice and a towel and Mrs. McKee began *yelling at* Tom. Mr. McKee and I quietly left the room.

事吵嘴，汤姆好像对威尔逊太太说，她没有任何权利去说黛西。

"黛西!黛西!黛西!"威尔逊太太叫道。"我想什么时候说她的名字，就什么时候说!黛西!黛西!黛——"

汤姆迅捷、断然地一拳打破了威尔逊太太的鼻子。血忽地一下溅得到处都是，每个人都开始尖叫起来。凯瑟琳跑去拿了些冰块和一条毛巾，麦基太太开始大声数落汤姆。麦基先生和我悄悄离开了屋子。

yell at sb.　向某人大声叫嚷，对某人叫喊

47

CHAPTER THREE My Strange Neighbor

Most evenings of the summer I could hear music coming from my neighbor's house. Obviously Mr. Gatsby enjoyed having parties and his parties were always big ones. Men and girls filled his huge house and beautiful gardens. They walked around slowly and whispered to each other; they drank wine and looked at the stars and swam in Gatsby's big swimming pool. The people who came to his parties didn't seem to have any work or study and, really, any worries. Sometimes his guests would arrive in the afternoon and swim in the ocean in front of his house. I would often watch his guests swimming and lying in the sun on the hot sand, or just riding his two boats.

On the weekends Gatsby's driver would take his big open car and carry groups of people *to and from* the city. I saw people coming at all times of the day, sometimes before nine in the morning and often long after midnight. His second car, and his second driver, would go and meet all the trains coming from New York. On *Mondays* ten servants, and an extra garden helper, would work all day to clean and repair the damage from the weekend's parties.

Two times every month Gatsby would have a really big party. The servants would cover the trees with colored lights and a dance floor would be built out in the yard. Gatsby hired

第三章 我的奇怪邻居

夏天的大多数晚上我都能听见音乐声从邻居家传来。显然，盖茨比先生喜欢举办聚会，而且聚会规模总是很大。男男女女挤满他的大宅子和美丽的花园。他们四处漫步，相互低语；他们饮酒、看星星或在盖茨比的大游泳池里游泳。来参加聚会的人好像无事可做，无须学习，好像也真的无任何烦恼。有时客人们会在下午来，然后在他房前的大海里游泳。我经常看着他的客人们游泳，躺在阳光下灸热的沙滩上或乘着他的两只船。

周末时，盖茨比的司机会开着大敞篷汽车，拉着成群的人往来于城郊之间。我看见一天里一直都有人来，有时从不到早晨九点常常持续到半夜过后很久。他的另一辆车和另一个司机将会去接所有从纽约来的火车。每到周一，总得有十个仆人和一个临时园丁花一整天时间来清理周末聚会的残局。

每月盖茨比举办两次真正的盛宴。仆人们会在树上装满彩灯，并在院子里修出一块跳舞场地。盖茨比雇了一大群音乐家为舞会演

to and from = back and forth
左右、来回。

mondays ['mʌndiz] 复数表示每个星期一。

a big group of musicians to play music for dancing. The house was filled with wonderful food and *dozens of* waiters, and the servants would also build a bar full of every kind of wine and other drink. His house was always full of excitement before these parties — I could feel the excitement from my house.

In the evening the last swimmers would come in from the beach and start dressing upstairs. Every minute many cars came from New York. The halls and rooms filled with girls in bright dresses with the newest, strangest styles of hair. Servants would carry drinks through the garden outside, and the air would fill with talk and laughter. When night came the lights in Gatsby's house would all turn on. The lights became brighter as the night became darker. The musicians became louder and louder. Wine glasses became empty, and filled, and empty again. And laughter became easier and easier.

The first night that I went to Gatsby's house I was one of the few guests who had actually been invited. A servant wearing a pale blue uniform came to my house one day with a surprising letter from his Mr. Gatsby. Gatsby, the letter said, would be very happy if I would come to his party that night. The letter said that he had seen me many times, and that he wanted to meet me.

Most of the people at his parties were not invited — they just went there. They *somehow* found Gatsby's house and once they were there they were introduced to Gatsby by someone

奏。屋子里满是丰盛的食物还有几十个侍者。仆人们还将搭起一个酒吧，摆满各种各样的酒和别的饮料。聚会举办之前，他家总是洋溢着兴奋——从我家就能感受到那种兴奋。

晚上，最后一批游泳者将会从海滨回到楼上开始更衣。每一分钟都有许多汽车从纽约来。大厅里、房间里挤满衣着鲜艳的女孩，梳着最新潮，最奇特的发型。仆人们穿过外边的花园搬送着饮料，空气中弥散着谈笑声。夜幕降临，盖茨比的家灯火齐明。随着夜色渐浓，灯也越来越亮，音乐家们演奏的声音也越来越大。酒杯空了，再满上，再喝干，于是欢笑声也越来越畅快了。

去盖茨比家的第一个晚上，我是真正受邀请的为数不多的客人之一。一天，一个穿着淡蓝色制服的仆人来到我家，拿着他主人盖茨比先生的请帖，这着实让我吃了一惊。上面盖茨比写道，如果我那晚能参加他家的聚会，他将不胜荣幸。信中还说他已看见过我多次，想结识我。

聚会上的大多数人都没受到邀请——只是他们自己去的。他们设法找到盖茨比的家，而一旦他们来了，就会被认识盖茨比的人介绍给

dozens of 表示人数为几十个或许多。

somehow ['sʌmhau] *adv.* 以某种方法，不知怎么的，由于某种未知的原因。

51

who knew him. Sometimes they came to the party and left again without *ever* having met Gatsby.

I went over to Gatsby's house at about seven o'clock. I felt nervous among all these people I didn't know, so I walked around looking for Gatsby. I asked many guests where he was, but they all stared at me in such a surprised way that I decided to go and sit at the bar. The bar was the only place in the garden where a single man could stand without looking strange.

I was at the bar for a long time. Finally I saw Jordan Baker come out of the house. She stood at the top of the stairs and looked around the garden.

"Hello!" I shouted, moving towards her.

"I thought you might be here," she answered, as I *walked up to* her. "I remembered that you lived just next door to — "

She was interrupted by two girls wearing yellow dresses. They stopped next to me at the bottom of the stairs and yelled up to her, "Sorry you didn't win."

They were talking about the golf competition the week before. She had lost in the last game.

"You don't know us," said one of the girls in yellow, "but we met you at another party here. It was about a month ago."

"You've changed the color of your hair since then," remarked Jordan.

盖茨比。有时他们来参加聚会后又离开了，根本就没看到过盖茨比。

　　大约七点钟时我去了盖茨比家。在这么多陌生人当中，我感觉紧张，于是我到处找盖茨比。我问过许多客人他在哪儿，但他们都非常吃惊地盯着我，于是我决定坐到酒吧里。酒吧是花园里惟一——处能让一个单身汉站在那儿不显奇怪的地方。

　　我在酒吧里呆了很长时间。最后我看见乔丹·贝克从屋里出来，她站在台阶的最高一级上环视着花园。

　　"你好！"我边喊边向她走去。

　　"我想你可能会在这儿，"我走近她时，她答道。"我记得你就住在隔壁——"

　　两个黄衣女郎打断了她的话。她们挨着我停在台阶下对台阶上的她喊道："很可惜你没能赢。"

　　她们说的是上个星期的那场高尔夫球赛，她在最后一局中输了。

　　"你不认识我们，"其中一个黄衣女孩说，"但我们在这儿的另一次聚会中见过你。大概是一个月前吧。"

　　"你们后来染过发了吧，"乔丹说。

ever ['evə] *adv.* 常用于否定句、疑问句或表示条件的从句，意为"在任何时候、从来"，有强调的意味。

walk up to 走到…的跟前

53

Jordan came down the stairs and put her thin arm in mine. We walked around the garden. A servant came out carrying wine and we sat down at a table with the two girls in yellow dresses and three men.

"I like these parties," said one of the girls. "I don't care what I do, so I always have a good time. Last time I came here I *ripped* my dress on a chair, and Gatsby asked me my name and address — a week later I received a box in the mail from Gatsby. There was a beautiful new dress in it. The dress must have cost more than two hundred dollars!"

"Did you keep the dress?" asked Jordan.

"Of course I did. I planned to wear it tonight, but it was too big in the top, and it had to be made smaller."

"There is something strange about Mr. Gatsby," said the other girl. "He *is worried about* having trouble with anybody."

The two girls and Jordan whispered together for a while and I talked with the men.

"Somebody told me they thought he killed a man once."

Excitement flowed through all of us hearing this. Gatsby was certainly a mysterious person.

"I heard," said one of the men, "that he was a German spy during the war."

"Oh no," said the girl, "he fought in the American army."

Everyone whispered about Gatsby, but all of the stories

乔丹下了台阶，用她那瘦瘦的胳膊挽着我。我们在花园里漫步，一个仆人端着酒走出来，我们和那两个黄衣女孩及三个男子坐在一张桌子边。

　　"我喜欢这些聚会，"其中一个女孩说。"我从不在乎我做什么，因此我总是玩得很开心。上次来时椅子挂破了我的礼服，盖茨比问了我的名字和住址———个星期后我收到盖茨比寄来的一个盒子，里面是一件漂亮的新礼服，一定值两百多美元！"

　　"你收下那件礼服了吗？"乔丹问。

　　"当然收下啦。我本打算今晚穿的，但领口太大了，得改小些。"

　　"盖茨比先生有点怪，"另一个女孩说。"他很担心得罪任何人。"

　　两个女孩和乔丹低语了一会儿，我和那几个男士聊了起来。

　　"有人告诉我，他们认为他曾杀过一个人。"

　　听到这，我们大家一阵兴奋，盖茨比一定是个神秘的人物。

　　"我听说战争期间他是一名德国间谍。"其中一个男子说。

　　"噢，不，"女孩说。"他在美国军队中参战。"

　　每个人都在低声议论着盖茨比，但是所

rip [rip] *vt.* （用利器）划破

be worried about 为…担心、发愁。例如：I'm worried about how the money was spent. 我担心这钱不知是怎么花掉的。

were different and nobody had any facts.

Dinner was now being served, and Jordan and I went to join her group of friends. They were sitting around a table on the far side of the garden. They were all respectable people from East Egg and they did not want to join together with the rest of the guests.

We sat with them for half an hour and then Jordan whispered to me, "Let's go somewhere else. This conversation is too *polite* and boring."

We got up, and she told her friends that we were going to find the host, because I was his neighbor and had never met him.

We looked at the bar first. It was full of people, but Gatsby was not there. We looked in the garden, at the pool and in the dining room, but we could not find him. Then we walked upstairs and opened an important-looking door. Inside was a huge library.

A fat, middle-aged man wearing large, round glasses was sitting on a large table in the library. He was staring at the bookshelves. He looked very drunk. When we entered he turned around and looked at us with excitement.

"What do you think?" he asked.

"Think about what?" I asked.

He moved his hands towards the bookshelves.

"About all the books! I thought they were all *fake books*

有的故事都不相同，也没人知道任何真实情况。

此时晚餐开始了，我和乔丹加入她那群朋友之中。他们远远地围坐在花园一边的桌子旁。他们都是从东卵镇来的受人尊重的人，都不想加入到其他的客人当中去。

我们跟他们一块坐了有半个小时，然后乔丹低声对我说，"我们到别的地方去，这些谈话太客套，太无聊。"

我们站起来，她告诉她的朋友说我们要去找主人，因为我是他的邻居却又从来没见过他。

我们先到酒吧里找，里面全是人，但盖茨比不在那儿。我们到花园、游泳池和餐厅里找，但始终没找到他。然后我们走上台阶，打开一扇模样尊贵的门，里面是一个很大的藏书室。

一个胖胖的、中等年纪的男子戴着一幅大圆眼镜坐在藏书室里一张大桌子上。他正盯着书架，看上去醉得很厉害。我们走进去时，他转过身来，兴奋地看着我们。

"你们觉得怎么样？"他问。
"觉得什么？"我问。
他把手移向书架。

"关于这些书！我原以为这些全是赝品，

polite [pə'lait] *adj.* 这里略含贬义，意思是"太过于客套的"。

and that they were here so that people would think this was a full library — but they're real!" He pulled down a heavy, *serious-looking book* and opened it. "They have pages and words and everything. Look! Let me show you."

He then became more serious. "Who brought you to this party?" he asked us. "A woman I met last night brought me here. I was drunk last night and I'm drunk tonight. I think I've been drunk for about a week now. I thought if I sat in the library I would stop drinking."

"Do you feel any better?" Jordan asked.

"I don't know yet. I've only been in the library for about an hour. Did I tell you that the books are real! They're — "

"You told us." Jordan said and we went back outside.

People were dancing now in the garden. The dancers moved around the dance floor slowly. A famous singer sang a song, and some actors acted a funny play, and wine was served in huge glasses — they were bigger than bowls. By midnight the fun was louder and wilder. All over the garden people were laughing and drinking. All the happiness seemed so empty.

About an hour later I was still with Jordan Baker. We sat at a table *where a man who* was about my age *and a girl who* laughed all the time *were sitting.* Now I didn't feel alone and was happy. I had drunk three glasses of wine, and the silly party suddenly seemed deep and important.

The man at the table looked at me and smiled.

摆在这儿是让人们以为这是一个充实的书房——可它们是真的!"他抽下来一本厚重的、装帧严肃的书,打开它。"书里有页码、有字,什么都有。看!我给你们看。"

然后他变得更严肃起来。"谁带你们来参加这个聚会的?"他问我们。"我昨晚认识的一个女人把我带到这儿。昨晚我喝醉了,今晚又喝醉了,我想这一周来我大概一直在醉,我想如果我坐在书房里,就不会再喝了。"

"你感觉好点了吗?"乔丹问。

"我还不知道。我只在书房呆了约一个小时。我有没有告诉过你们这些书是真的?它们是——"

"你告诉过我们啦。"乔丹说完,我们又回到外面。

现在人们正在花园里跳舞。他们绕着舞池悠悠旋转。一位有名的歌星正在演唱,几个演员在表演一个滑稽剧,酒用比碗还大的玻璃杯端上来。夜半时分娱乐气氛越来越喧闹,也越来越离谱。整个花园里所有的人都在笑着,饮着。所有的欢乐好像都是如此空洞。

·大约一个小时后我仍和乔丹·贝克呆在一块儿。我们坐到一张桌边,一位年龄与我相仿的男子和一个一直在笑的女孩也坐在桌边。如今我不再感觉孤独,而是很快活。我喝了三杯酒之后,这愚蠢的聚会就突然间似乎变得重要而意味深长起来。

桌边的那个男子看看我,笑了起来。

fake book 赝品

serious-looking book 外观、装帧看上去是严肃的书。

where a man who... and a girl who... were sitting 由 where引出的修饰table的定语从句中,又含有两个who引出的定语从句,分别修饰man和girl。

"I think I have seen you before," he said politely. "Were you in the army during the war? I think we were in the same unit — were you in the First Division?"

"Why, yes I was." I was surprised.

The man and I talked for a while about some of the places we had been in the war. I learned that he lived in this neighborhood also, because he told me that he had just bought an airplane that could land in the water. He told me that he was going to try it in the morning.

"Do you want to fly with me tomorrow, young fellow?" he asked.

I wanted to go and accepted. I was about to ask his name when Jordan said to me, "Having a good time now?"

I smiled and turned to my new friend. "This party is strange for me. I don't even know the host. I haven't met him yet. I live over there — " I turned around and pointed my hand toward my house, " — and this man, Gatsby, sent over his servant with an invitation."

For a moment the man *I was talking to* looked at me as if he didn't understand. "I'm Gatsby," he said suddenly.

"What!" I cried. "Oh, I didn't — I'm so sorry."

"*I thought* you knew, young fellow. I'm sorry — I suppose I'm not a very good host."

He smiled at me. His smiles had a quality of comfort in it. It was a smile that you may only see four or five times in life.

"我觉得以前见过您。"他有礼貌地说。"战争期间，你参军了吗?我想我们是一个部队的——你是在第一师吗?"

"啊，是的。"我很吃惊。

那个人和我谈了一会儿我们参战的一些地方的情况。我了解到他也住在这附近，因为他告诉我他刚买了一架可以在水上降落的飞机，打算早上试飞。

"老兄，明天你想和我一块试飞吗?"他问。

我想去，于是就答应了。我正要问他的名字，这时乔丹对我说话了，"现在玩得开心吗?"

我笑着转向这位新朋友。"这样的聚会对我来说很新奇，我甚至还不认识主人，我还没见到他，我就住那边——"我转过身，用手指向我的房子，"——这位盖茨比派仆人送过去一张请帖。"

跟我说话的那个男子看了我一会儿，好像很不明白。"我就是盖茨比。"他突然说。

"什么!"我叫了起来。"噢，我不——对不起。"

"我还以为你认识我，老兄。对不起——我想我不是一个很好的主人。"

他对我笑了。他的笑里带有安慰的意味，这种笑你一生中也许只能遇上四五回，他的笑

I was talking to 是主语man 的定语从句。

I thought... 有"本来认为/以为"的意思，是说话者原来的一种猜测，引出宾语从句。

61

His smile seemed to say that the whole world was good and that you were also good. His smile understood you and it believed you.

His smile disappeared, and I looked at Mr. Gatsby for the first time. He was a handsome young man, about thirty years old and dressed very well. He spoke very politely and it was a little funny to me; most men his age were not so polite. He spoke as if he was carefully choosing his words.

Before I could talk to Gatsby more a helper came over and told him that someone in Chicago was calling him on the telephone.

"Excuse me. I will come back later," he politely said.

After he left I turned to Jordan. I wanted to *tell* her *of* my surprise. I had expected Gatsby to be quite different. He was so young; I thought he would be older and fatter.

"Who is he?" I asked Jordan.

"I don't know. He's just a man named Gatsby."

"Where is he from? And what does he do?"

"Now you want to talk about him also. Everyone here talks about him, but nobody knows him." She said. "He told me once he had been to Oxford University, but I don't believe him."

"Why don't you?"

"I don't know. I just don't. He does not seem like an Oxford man."

好像是在说这整个世界都是美好的，你也是美好的。他的笑显示出他了解你，信任你。

他的微笑消失后，我才第一次看了看盖茨比先生。他英俊、年轻，三十岁左右，衣着考究。他说话很有礼貌，这让人感觉有点奇怪；大多数这个年龄的男人都没有这么客气。他说话时好像字斟句酌。

还没等我跟盖茨比说更多的话，一个仆人就走过来告诉他芝加哥有人打电话过来。

"对不起，我一会儿就回来。"他客客气气地说。

他走后，我转向乔丹。我想告诉她我的惊讶，我原来想像的盖茨比很不一样。他很年轻；而我以为他会老一点，胖一点。

"他是谁?"我问乔丹。

"我不知道，他只是一个叫盖茨比的男人。"

"他从哪儿来，又是干什么的?"

"现在你也想谈论他了，这儿的每个人都谈论他，但是没人了解他。"她说。"有一次他告诉我他上过牛津大学，但我不相信。"

"你为什么不相信呢?"

"不知道，我就是不相信。他不像个牛津大学的学生。"

tell of = tell about 讲述

There was truly something very strange about Gatsby's past life. He was so rich and he bought a huge house on *Long Island Sound* where they *threw parties,* certainly expensive ones, every few days? Most rich people had rich and famous families, but nobody knew anything about Gatsby's family.

The band began playing some loud music. I looked up and saw Gatsby. He was standing alone at the top of the stairs and looking out at all the people. His eyes looked happy.

I watched him for a long time, but I could not see *anything strange* about him. He seemed different only because he was not drinking wine like his guests were. As the guests became wilder, he became more calm and correct.

Gatsby's helper suddenly came up to us.

"Miss Baker?" he said. "Excuse me, but Mr. Gatsby would like to speak to you alone." Jordan looked extremely surprised and followed the helper into the house.

An hour later I decided to go home. As I waited for the servants to get my hat, the door of the library opened and Jordan and Gatsby came out together. He was speaking excitedly to her.

Jordan *came over to* me and whispered, "I've just heard the strangest thing. How long were we in there?"

"About an hour." I said.

"It was very strange, but I promised I wouldn't tell anybody. Please come and see me soon." She then hurried off.

关于盖茨比过去的生活确实很奇怪。他这么富裕，在长岛海湾买了这么大的房子，每几天举行一次聚会，当然是消费很高的聚会。大多数富人都有富裕而有名望的家庭，但是没人知道盖茨比家庭的任何情况。

乐队开始演奏一些响亮的音乐。我抬起头，看见了盖茨比。他一个人站在台阶上，看着所有的人，眼睛里似乎洋溢着欢乐。

我观察了他很长一会儿，但没能看出他的任何奇怪之处。他似乎有些不同，只是因为他没有像他的客人们那样在喝酒。客人们越来越狂乱的时候，他却变得更平静更理智。

盖茨比的仆人突然向我们走过来。

"是贝克小姐吗？"他说。"对不起，盖茨比先生想单独跟您谈谈。"乔丹显得非常吃惊，跟着仆人进了屋子。

一小时后，我决定回去了。在我等着仆人去给我取帽子时，书房的门开了，乔丹和盖茨比一起走出来，他正兴奋地对她说着什么。

乔丹朝我走过来后低声说，"我刚才听说一件最离奇的事情。我们在那里呆了多久？"

"一小时左右吧。"我说。

"太离奇了，但我答应过不告诉任何人。请早点来看我。"说完她匆匆离去了。

Long Island Sound 长岛海峡，位于美国康涅狄格州与长岛之间的水域。

throw party 用于口语中，意思是"举行（宴会等）"。例如：He threw a dance celebration for them. 他为她们举行舞会（庆祝会）。

anything strange 修饰不定代词的形容词，跟在不定代词之后。意为"奇怪的事情"。

came over to 走过来到…

The party was over and the last of Gatsby's guests were standing all around him. I said goodnight to him and apologized for not finding him earlier in the evening.

"No apology needed," he said eagerly. "And don't *forget* to come over tomorrow at nine. We're going to fly in the sea-plane."

His helper came up behind him and said, "Philadelphia wants you on the phone, sir."

"I'll come in a minute... Good night, young fellow... Good night." He smiled, and I was glad that I was one of the last to leave; it seemed that Gatsby wanted it all the time.

Reading what I have written so far again, it seems that the three evenings I have described are all that were *interesting* to me. This is not true. When they happened these nights seemed very common. They were the same as many of the events in my busy summer. Later I realized just how important these events were.

I spent most of my time this summer working. My days were usually about the same. I went to work in early morning, and worked until the evening. I liked the other workers and always ate lunch with them and talked about work and life. After work I usually ate dinner and then I went to the library and studied for an hour or two. I learned a lot about money matters that summer. After that I would usually walk to the train station and get on the fast train back to West Egg.

聚会结束了，最后一批客人都围在盖茨比的身旁。我跟他道晚安，并道歉晚上没能及早找到他。

"不必道歉，"他急切地说。"别忘了明天九点过来，我们要试飞水上飞机。"

仆人走到他身后说："先生，费城来电话找您。"

他微笑着说："我一会儿就来……晚安，老兄……晚安。"我很高兴我是最后离开的几个，盖茨比好像一直就想这样。

重读了一遍目前我所写的这些，好像我所有感兴趣的，就是我所描述的这三个晚上。并非如此，这些晚上发生的事似乎都很普通，就跟繁忙的夏日里所发生的许多事情一样普通，只是后来我才意识到这些事情有多么重要。

这个夏天，我把大部分时间都花在工作上。每天差不多都是一样，一大早去上班，一直工作到晚上。我喜欢其他员工，总是和他们一块吃午餐、谈论工作和生活。下班后，我通常是吃了晚饭就去书房学习一两个钟头。那年夏天我学了不少金融方面的知识。而后，我通常走到火车站，坐快车回到西卵镇。

forget [fə'get] *v.* 后接不定式表示"忘了要做某事"（实际上没有做）。后接动名词表示"忘了已做过的事"（实际上已经做了）。

interesting ['intristiŋ] *adj.* 事物本身"有趣的、令人感兴趣的"。注意它与interested的区别，interested表示某人"感兴趣的、注意的、关心的"。例如：This film is very interesting. 这部电影很有趣。I'm very interested in this film. 我对这部电影很感兴趣。

I did not see Jordan Baker for about a month. In the middle of the summer I saw her again at the Buchanans' house. We began to see each other often. I liked to go places with her because she was a famous golf player and I felt important when I was with her. Many people knew her name and they began to know my name also. After a while I began to like her. I didn't love her, but I wanted to understand her. I knew that her cold, scolding face was just a mask. Under the mask she was hiding something — and one day I found what it was.

One day we went to a party together in the city. When we were there she left a car that she had borrowed from her friend out in the rain *with the windows open*. Because of her mistake the inside was destroyed, but I later heard her lie about it. When I heard her lie I remembered the story about her that I could not remember the night that I met her at Daisy's house. Many people had said that she cheated in her first big golf game; the news about her cheating was almost written *in the newspapers*. People thought that she had moved her ball from a bad place to a good place in order to win.

Yes, Jordan Baker was not an honest person. She hated to lose, in sports and in all of life, so she cheated and lied to get what she wanted. Her proud and cold face was hiding all these lies.

Later I realized that she did not like to talk with clever people. She felt safer talking with people who would not ask

我大约有一个月没见到乔丹·贝克了。仲夏时节我在布坎南家又见过她一次，此后我们开始经常见面。我喜欢跟她到许多地方去，因为她是著名的高尔夫球手，跟她在一块儿时，我感觉自己很了不起。许多人知道她的名字，也开始知道我的名字。一段时间后，我开始喜欢上她了。我并不爱她，但我想了解她。我知道她那张冷冰冰、带有嘲讽的脸只是一张面具，在那张面具下面她在隐藏着什么——总有一天我会发现那是什么。

一天，我们一块去市里参加聚会。她跟朋友借了一辆车，到了那儿，她没关车窗就把车放在雨中了。就因为她的疏忽，车内遭到了破坏，但我后来听说她对此撒了个谎。当我听到她撒的这个谎时，我记起了在黛西家遇见她的那晚我没有记起来的与她有关的事情。很多人说过她在第一次大型高尔夫球赛中作了弊；关于她作弊的消息差点儿上了报。人们认为她为了赢得比赛而把她的球从一个不利的地方移到了一个有利的地方。

是的，乔丹·贝克不是个诚实的人。她憎恨在比赛和整个一生中失败，因此她作弊、撒谎以得到她想要的东西。她那张骄傲而冰冷的脸下隐藏着所有这些谎言。

后来我意识到她不喜欢和精明的人谈话。她觉得和那些不问她行为的人谈话会更安全

with the windows open 介词短语作定语修饰car。

in the newspapers 在报纸上。这里in不能用on。

69

questions about her actions. She liked me perhaps because I did not care that she lied. Women have many reasons to lie in this world; their life was hard and unfair. I could not be *angry about* a woman lying — I felt sorry, and then I forgot.

While at the party we had a strange conversation about driving a car. She was driving too close to some workmen on the road and it made me feel nervous.

"You should drive more carefully," I told her.

"I am careful."

"No, you're not careful."

"Well, other people are and they will jump *out of* my *way*."

"*What if* those people are also careless? What will you do if you meet a careless person?"

"I hope I never will," she answered. "I hate careless people. That's why I like you."

She stared straight ahead with her gray eyes. I looked at her closely and for a moment I thought that I loved her.

I wanted to tell her, but my mind often *stopped me from* doing what I wanted to do. Before I could love her I had to end my relationship with my girlfriend in the Midwest. I had been writing letters to her once a week and I had to stop before moving to a different woman or else I would not feel honest. Being honest is very important to me.

些。她喜欢我也许是因为我不在意她撒谎。女人们在这个世界上有很多撒谎的理由；生活对她们来说很艰难、很不公平。我不能对一个撒谎的女人生气——我只能觉得遗憾，然后就忘了。

聚会上我们有过一段关于驾驶汽车的奇怪谈话。她把车开得离路上的几个工人太近了，这使我感到很紧张。

"你应该开得再小心一点。"我告诉她。

"我小心啦。"

"不，你不小心。"

"那，别人小心了，他们会让开的。"

"如果这些人也不小心呢？如果碰到一个粗心的人你会做出什么事来？"

"但愿我永远不会碰到。"她答道。"我讨厌粗心的人，这就是为什么我喜欢你。"

她那双灰色的眼睛直直地盯着前方，我靠近点儿看着她，一时间我想我想爱她。

我想告诉她，但我的思想经常阻止我干自己想干的事。在我能够去爱她之前，我得结束与中西部那个女朋友的关系。一直以来我一周写一封信给她，我得先停止给她写信，然后才能转向另一个女人，否则我会觉得自己不诚实，而做诚实的人对我来说很重要。

angry about 因为…事情而生气

out of the way 不挡道、不碍事。反义短语为 in the way 挡道的、碍事的。

what if 如果…将会怎么样；即使…

stop sb. from 后接动词，表示"阻止某人做某事"。

71

CHAPTER FOUR Daisy and Gatsby

G atsby's *fancy* car drove up to my door one morning in
July. He never visited me before, though I had already attended two parties at his house, flown with him in his
seaplane once and sat on his private beach often.

"Good morning, young fellow. Would you like to drive into
New York today and have lunch with me? I thought we could
drive into the city together."

Gatsby saw me admiring his beautiful car.

"It's pretty, isn't it? You've seen it before, haven't you?"

Of course, I'd seen it. Everybody in West Egg had seen it.
It was bright yellow, with green leather seats. We jumped in
and quickly drove off.

I had talked with Gatsby many times in the past month. I
was disappointed to find out that he did not have much interesting to say. When I first met him I felt that he was a very
important person, a person who would help to change the
world. Now this feeling disappeared. Now he was just the man
who owned the big, fancy house next door.

My feelings about him changed when we took this ride. It
was a very surprising ride. As we talked, he seemed full of
doubt and very strange, and he began to speak in broken sen-
tences. "Look here, young fellow," he finally said, "Tell me
the truth. What is your *opinion* of me?"

第四章　黛西与盖茨比

七月的一个早晨，盖茨比开着别致的小车来到我门前。他以前从没拜访过我，虽然我去他家参加过两次聚会，和他飞过一次他的水上飞机，还经常坐在他家的私人海滩上。

"早上好，老兄。你今天愿意和我一块儿开车去纽约吃午饭吗？我想我们可以开车一块进城。"

盖茨比看见我正羡慕地看着他的漂亮汽车。

"挺漂亮，是不是？你以前见过的，不是吗？"

我当然见过它。西卵镇的每一个人都见过它，鲜黄的车身，绿皮座位。我们跳进汽车，很快就出发了。

上月里我和盖茨比聊过多次。我发现他没有多少有趣的事说给我听，这让我很失望。我第一次见他时觉得他是一个很了不起的人物，愿意帮助人们改变这个世界。现在这种感觉消失了，他仅仅是隔壁一家漂亮大房子的主人。

我对他的感觉在这次同车之行中变了。这是一次非常令人惊讶的出行。我们谈话时，他似乎对自己很没有把握，显得莫名其妙，并且说话也开始吞吞吐吐。"看，老兄，"他最后说，"跟我说实话。你对我怎么看？"

fancy ['fænsi] *adj.* 别致的、花哨的

who owned the big, fancy house next door 定语从句，修饰the man。

opinion [ə'pinjən] *n.* 文中表示"评价、印象"之意

73

I began to say some common things that would not make him happy or angry.

"Well, I want to tell you something about myself," he said. "I don't want you to think bad things about me because of all the stories people say about me. I will tell you the true story."

"I was born in the Middle West. My parents were wealthy people, but they are all dead now. I grew up in America, but was educated in England at Oxford University, because all the men in my family always went to Oxford."

He looked at me in a strange way — and I understood why Miss Baker had thought he was *lying* about attending Oxford. It was because he said "educated at Oxford" too quickly; he said it so that I did not have any time to question him.

"After my family all died, I received a lot of money. *Since then* I have lived like a king in all of the capitals of Europe — Paris, Rome, Venice. I spent time buying jewels and hunting wild animals; I even painted a little. Mostly I tried to forget something very sad that happened to me a long time ago."

I didn't believe what he was saying and I wanted to laugh at him, but, to be polite, I was silent.

"Then the war started, young fellow. I was happy, and I tried very hard to die; I always ran to the front of the fighting, but some luck or magic always seemed to keep me alive. I became a captain when the war began, and I led a group of

我开始泛泛而谈，既不让他高兴，也不使他生气。

　　"呃，我想告诉你我自己的一些事，"他说。"我不想因为人们说的所有关于我的故事而让你把我往坏处想。我要告诉你真相。"

　　"我出生在中西部，我的父母很有钱，但他们现在都死了。我在美国长大，但是在英国牛津大学受教育，因为我家里的所有人都是在牛津上大学。"

　　他用令人奇怪的眼神看着我——我明白了贝克小姐为什么曾认为他上过牛津大学是撒谎。因为他说"在牛津受教育"时太快；他这样说好让我没时间去追问他。

　　"我家里所有人死后，我继承了一大笔钱。从那时起，我像个国王那样到欧洲各国的著名都市居住——巴黎、罗马、威尼斯。我把时间花在买珠宝和打猎上；我还画点儿画。我主要是想尽力忘掉很久以前我所遭遇的非常心酸的事。"

　　我不相信他说的话，心里想笑，但出于礼貌，我保持了沉默。

　　"然后，战争爆发了，老兄。我很高兴，我竭力去死；我总是冲到战斗的最前面，但好像总有某种运气或魔法让我活了下来。战争开始时我成为一名中尉，领导一队机枪兵。在德国的森林里我率领士兵（远远地跑在其他士兵

since then 从那时到现在。多用于完成时态的句子里。

75

machine-gun soldiers. In the forests of Germany I led my men far in front of the other soldiers. We fought there for two days and two nights, and we killed more than a hundred and thirty Germans. When the other American soldiers finally found us, they saw *piles of* dead Germans everywhere. After that every government in Europe, and America also, gave me a medal."

Gatsby then reached into his pocket and pulled out a war medal.

"This medal is the one from the government of Montenegro."

I was shocked, the medal looked real. On the medal was written "Major Jay Gatsby — For Courage in Battle."

"Here's another thing that I always carry. It is a picture to remember my life at Oxford University."

He handed me a photograph of five or six young men standing together. In the background were two towers. Gatsby was in the middle; he looked a little younger, but it was definitely Gatsby.

Suddenly I believed him, everything he said was true! I imagined his palace in Rome; I imagined him hunting; I imagined him staring into a box of expensive, dark jewels and trying to forget the pain in his broken heart.

"Today I want to ask you to help me," he said, "so I thought you should know more about my life." For a minute he stopped speaking.

前面）。我们战斗了两天两夜，打死了一百三十多名德军。当最后其他美国士兵找到我们时，发现到处都堆着德军的尸体。此后欧洲各国政府，还有美国，都给我授过勋章。"

然后盖茨比伸手从衣袋里掏出一块战斗勋章。

"这块勋章是蒙特内格罗政府授予的。"

我很震惊，勋章像是真的。上面写着"杰伊·盖茨比少校——战斗勇士。"

"这里还有一样我总是随身带的东西。一张我在牛津大学的生活纪念照。"

他递给我一张照片，照片上五六个年轻人站在一起，背景是两座塔楼。盖茨比站在中间；他看上去稍年轻些，但确实是盖茨比。

突然间我相信了他，他说的所有话都是真的！我想像着他在罗马的豪宅，想像他在打猎，想像着他正盯着一盒子昂贵的、色彩浓艳的珠宝，试图忘掉那颗破碎的心中的痛苦。

"今天我想请您帮个忙，"他说，"因此我觉得您应该多了解我的生活。"他停了一会儿。

a pile of 一大堆的。piles of 一堆堆的

"I won't tell you now. You'll hear about it later."

"At lunch?"

"No, later this afternoon. I *found out* that you are planning to have tea with Jordan Baker after lunch."

"Do you mean that you are in love with Miss Baker?" I asked surprised.

"No, young fellow, I'm not. However, Miss Baker will speak to you about this affair."

I did not know what "this affair" was, but I *was annoyed at* Gatsby. I was not going to tea with Jordan so that we could discuss Mr. Jay Gatsby.

Gatsby would not say another word about what he wanted. We continued driving. As we passed the dirty train tracks I saw Mrs. Wilson fixing a car with her usual animal energy.

Gatsby was driving quite fast.

After a moment I heard the sound of a motorcycle. A policeman *rode up* next *to* us and Gatsby stopped the car. He then pulled a white card out of his pocket and handed it to the policeman.

"Excuse me, Mr. Gatsby!" said the policeman when he looked at the card. "I'll know that this car is yours next time. Sorry to trouble you!" The policeman then rode away.

"What did you show him?" I asked. "Was it the picture of you at Oxford?"

"No, I helped the Chief of Police before, and he sends

"我现在不告诉您，您以后会听说的。"

"午饭时吗？"

"不，是下午以后。我发现您打算午饭后和乔丹·贝克喝茶。"

"你意思是说你爱上贝克小姐啦？"我吃惊地问。

"不，老兄，我没有。不过，这件事贝克小姐会跟您说的。"

我不知道"这件事"是什么，但我对盖茨比感到厌烦。我约乔丹喝茶并不是为了和她谈论杰伊·盖茨比先生。

对他想做什么事盖茨比不愿再多说一个字。我们开车继续前行。当我们经过脏兮兮的铁轨时，我看见威尔逊太太正一如既往地用她那股牲口般的劲头修车。

盖茨比开车相当快。

一会儿我听到一辆摩托车的声音。一个警察驱车赶到我们旁边，盖茨比停下车。然后他从口袋里掏出一张白色卡片递给警察。

"对不起，盖茨比先生！"警察看着卡片说。"下次我就知道这是您的车啦。对不起，打扰了！"接着警察就开车走了。

"您给他看的是什么？"我问。"是在牛津大学的照片吗？"

"不，我以前帮过警察局长，他每年圣诞

fine out 找出、发现、查明（真相）fine out a secret 发现秘密

be annoyed at sb. = be annoyed with sb. 对某人生气

ride up to 骑马（坐车）赶到…跟前

79

me a card every year at Christmas."

Gatsby and I stopped for lunch at a little restaurant in the middle of the city. Another man came to meet us. He was a small man with small eyes and a flat nose; he looked about forty years old.

"Mr. Carraway, let me introduce my friend Mr. Wolfshiem."

We sat down and ordered some food.

"I like this restaurant," said Mr. Wolfshiem. "But the restaurant across the street is even better."

"It's too hot there," said Gatsby.

"Yes, it's hot and small. But it is also full of memories. It makes me think about dead friends. I will never forget sitting in that restaurant the night that Rosy Rosenthal was shot. Six friends were all sitting at the table, and Rosy had been drinking beer and eating all the evening. At four-thirty in the morning a waiter came over to Rosy with a strange look on his face. He said that somebody wanted to talk with him outside. It sounded strange, so I told him not to go."

"Did he go?" I asked.

"Yes, he went. Before going out the door he turned around and said to me 'Don't let the waiter *take away* my coffee.' Then he went outside into the street, and we heard gunshots. Some men had shot him four times in his chest and ran away."

He suddenly looked at me and said, "I heard that you

节都送我一张卡片。"

盖茨比和我在市中心一家小饭馆停车吃午饭。另一个男子走过来迎接我们。他是个小眼睛、塌鼻子的小个子；看上去大约四十岁。

"卡罗威先生，让我来介绍一下我的朋友沃尔夫山姆先生。"

我们坐下来，点了饭菜。

"我喜欢这个饭馆，"沃尔夫山姆先生说。"但街对面那家饭馆更好啦。"

"那儿太热了，"盖茨比说。

"对，又热又小。但却充满了回忆，它让我想起那些死去的朋友，我永远忘不了坐在那个饭店里罗西·罗森塔尔被枪杀的那个晚上。六个朋友都坐在桌边，整个晚上罗西一直在喝啤酒、吃东西。凌晨4点30分时一个脸上带着一种奇怪表情的侍者走到罗西身边，告诉他外面有人想跟他说话。这听起来很怪，因此我告诉他别去。"

"他去了吗？"我问。

"是的，他去了。还没走到门外时他转过身对我说'别让侍者撤走我的咖啡。'然后就出去走到街上，接着我们就听到了枪声。有人朝他胸部开了四枪后就跑了。"

他突然看着我说："我听说你正在找一

take away 拿走；带走。例如：He took the food away. 他拿走了食物。

81

are looking for a connection in business."

Gatsby quickly answered for me. "No, Meyer, this is a different man! We'll talk about that business some other time."

Before we finished eating our meal Gatsby looked at his watch, jumped up and hurried out of the room.

"He has to use the telephone," said Mr. Wolfshiem. "It's a business matter. He's a fine young fellow, isn't he? A true gentleman, he went to Oxford University in England."

"Have you known him for a long time?" I asked.

"Yes, for many years. I met him *a little bit* after the war, and we have done a lot of business together — He's helped me and I've helped him."

When Gatsby returned, Wolfshiem stood up.

"I have to go. I will leave you two young men to discuss your young ladies and sports," he said. I stood up and we shook hands.

"Meyer Wolfshiem is an important man in this area," said Gatsby after Wolfshiem left.

"What's his business? How did he *make* all his *money*?"

"Oh, in many ways — " Gatsby said while looking at the ground. "Do you remember the big baseball cheat in 1919? Meyer did that; he cheated a lot of people into giving him money. He really became rich from it."

I was shocked. "Why isn't he in prison?"

个生意关系户。"

盖茨比赶紧替我回答。"不，迈耶，这不是那个人！我们改天再谈那笔生意吧。"

我们还没吃完饭时，盖茨比看看表，跳起来，匆匆走出了屋子。

"他得打电话。"沃尔夫山姆先生说。"是生意上的事。他是个好小伙子，是不是？一位真正的绅士，他在英国上过牛津大学。"

"你认识他很长时间了吗？"我问。

"是的，好多年了。战后我不常见到他，我们一起做过很多生意——他帮过我，我也帮过他。"

盖茨比回来时，沃尔夫山姆站了起来。
"我得走了。让你们年轻人谈谈你们的年轻姑娘和体育吧。"他说。我站起来，我俩握了握手。

沃尔夫山姆走后，盖茨比说："迈耶·沃尔夫山姆是这一带的重要人物。"

"他做什么生意？他的钱都是怎么赚的？"

"噢，用各种方法——"盖茨比看着地面说。"你还记得1919年那次很大的棒球诈骗事件吗？就是迈耶做的，他骗了许多人给他钱。他真正是从这里面发财的。"

我惊呆了。"为什么他没坐牢？"

a little bit = a little 或 a bit。表示"一点；稍微"之意。
make money 赚钱、发财。
He makes money in the stock market. 他炒股赚钱。

83

"They can't prove that he did it, young fellow. He is a clever man."

I insisted on paying for lunch. When the waiter came over I saw Tom Buchanan across the room.

"Come with me for a minute," I said to Gatsby. "I have to *say hello to* a friend."

Tom jumped up eagerly when he saw us. *"What have you been doing recently?"* he said. " Daisy is angry because you haven't called."

"Sorry." I said, "This is my friend Mr. Gatsby."

They shook hands. A strange and troubled look appeared on Gatsby's face.

"Why are you here?" Tom demanded of me. "How did you to come this far just to eat?"

"I was having lunch with Mr. Gatsby here — "

I turned towards Mr. Gatsby, but he had left.

Later that afternoon, I went to tea with Jordan Baker. She told me this story:

The story was in Louisville, the small town where she was a child; the time was when the United States joined the Great War.

Jordan began telling her story, "In October of 1917, I was walking *down* the street where Daisy Fay house was. She was eighteen then, and I was sixteen. She was the most popular young girl in all of Louisville and I greatly admired her. She

"他们不能证明是他做的，老兄。他很精明。"

这顿午饭钱我坚持要付。侍者走过来时我看见汤姆·布坎南从屋里穿过。

"跟我来一下，"我对盖茨比说。"我得跟一个朋友打声招呼。"

汤姆看见我们时，急忙跳起来。"你最近去哪儿忙了？"他说。"因为你不打电话，黛西都生气了。"

"对不起。"我说，"这是我的朋友盖茨比先生。"

他们握了握手。盖茨比的脸上露出奇怪而不安的表情。

"你怎么在这儿？"汤姆问我。"你怎么大老远来这就是为了吃顿饭？"

"我在这儿和盖茨比先生一块吃午饭——"

我转向盖茨比先生，但他已经走了。

那天下午晚些时候，我去和乔丹·贝克一块喝茶，她告诉了我这个故事：

故事发生在路易斯维尔，她小时候生活过的一个小镇；时间是在美国参加世界大战的时候。

乔丹开始讲她的故事，"1917年10月，我正走在黛西·费伊家所在的大街上。她那时十八岁，我十六岁。她是整个路易斯维尔最出风头的年轻姑娘，我很崇拜她。她平时总穿白色衣服，她还有辆白色小轿车。她家的电话整

say hello to sb. 向某人问候。如：My wife joins me in saying hello to you. 我夫人也让我给您带好儿。

What have you been doing recently? 现在完成进行时，表示 "一直在做…"。本句意为 "你最近一直在干什么呢？"

down [daun] *prep.* 沿、循、顺。He walked down the hall to the elevator. 他们沿着走廊向电梯走去。

usually dressed in white, and she had a little white car. All day long the telephone in her house rang and many excited young army captains asked to take her out to dinner and dancing that night.

That day I saw her outside, sitting in her car. She was sitting with a man I had never seen before; he was a captain in the army. They were so interested in each other that she didn't see me until I was very close to her.

"Hello, Jordan," she called. "Please come over here."

She asked me if I was going to the factory to sew things for the soldiers. I was. She then asked me if I would tell the factory that she was busy and could not come to work that day. While she was speaking to me, the young man looked at her the way that all the young girls wanted men to look at them. The man's name was Jay Gatsby, and after that day I didn't see him again for a long time — more than four years — even after I went to parties at his house and met him again, I still didn't realize it was the man in the car with Daisy.

That was in 1917. By the next year I also had young men who were interested in me. I started to play in golf competitions, and I didn't see Daisy very often. I heard a story that her mother had found her preparing to leave her house one night to go to New York and say goodbye to a soldier who was going away to France to fight. Of course they stopped her from going.

She was unhappy for a while, but by the next fall she was

天响个不停，那天晚上很多兴奋的年轻军官邀请她出去吃饭和跳舞。

那天，我看见她坐着汽车出去了。她和一个我以前从未见过的男子坐在一起；那人是一名军官。他们彼此很喜欢，以致直到我走得很近时她才看见我。

"你好，乔丹，"她喊道。"请到这儿来。"

她问我是否要去工厂为士兵们干针线活。我说是。然后她又问我是否愿意告诉工厂，她那天太忙，不能来上班了。她对我说话时，那个年轻人看着她，那种注视方式是所有年轻女孩都想得到的。那个男人的名字叫杰伊·盖茨比，从那以后好长时间我再也没看见过他——四年多吧——甚至我去他家参加聚会又一次见到他时，我仍没意识到他就是和黛西呆在车里的那个人。

那是在1917年。到了第二年我也有了几个喜欢我的年轻男子。我开始参加高尔夫球赛，不再经常见到黛西。我听说一天晚上她母亲发现她准备离家去纽约，为到法国参战的一个士兵送行。当然他们没让她去。

她难过了一段时间，但到第二年秋天，

again happy, very happy. In February I heard that she was going to get married and in June she married Tom Buchanan of Chicago. Their wedding was the most fancy wedding that had ever happened in Louisville. Tom drove down to Louisville with a hundred friends in four private buses. He even rented a whole floor of a hotel and the day before the wedding he gave her some jewels that cost three hundred thousand dollars.

I was Daisy's helper at the wedding. Strangely, the night before the wedding I could not find her. Finally I came into her room half an hour before the big dinner party. I found her lying on her bed; she was as lovely as a flower and *as drunk as a monkey*. In one hand she had an empty bottle of wine and her other hand grasped a letter.

"I've never drank wine before," she said.

"What's wrong, Daisy?" I asked. I was worried because I'd never seen a girl so drunk before.

"Come here, my friend." She put her hand in the garbage basket and pulled out the jewels that Tom had given her. "Take this garbage downstairs and give them back to who they belong to. Tell everybody that Daisy isn't getting married. Yell loudly, 'Daisy has changed her mind!'"

She began to cry — and she cried and cried and cried. I ran out and found her mother's helper, and we locked the door and put Daisy into a cold bath. She wouldn't put the letter down. She even took it into the bath with her, until it was just

她又快活起来了，而且非常快活。二月里我听说她准备结婚，六月份嫁给芝加哥的汤姆·布坎南。他们的婚礼是曾在路易斯维尔举办过的最豪华的一场婚礼。汤姆带着一百个朋友分乘四辆私人大客车一直开到路易斯维尔。他甚至还租了旅馆里的整个一层楼，婚礼前一天他送给她一些价值三十万美元的珠宝首饰。

婚礼上，我是黛西的伴娘。奇怪的是，婚礼前夜我找不到她了。最后在大型晚宴之前半小时，我进了她的房间。我发现她躺在床上，貌美如花，酩酊大醉。她一只手拿着一个空酒瓶，另一只手攥着一封信。

"我以前从没喝过酒，"她说。

"怎么啦，黛西？"我问。我很担心，因为我以前从没见过一个女孩醉成这样。

"过来，朋友。"她把手伸进垃圾篓，拽出汤姆给她的珠宝。"把这些垃圾拿下楼，是谁的就还给谁。告诉大家黛西不打算结婚了，大声喊：'黛西改变主意啦!'"

她开始哭——哭啊，哭啊，哭啊。我跑出去，找到她妈妈的仆人，然后我们锁上门，拉黛西去洗冷水澡。她不肯放下那封信，还把它带到澡盆里，直到它变成一个湿纸团。

as drank as a monkey 酩酊大醉

89

a wet ball.

But she didn't talk any more about the letter. We cleaned her, put ice on her head, and put her back into her dress. A half an hour later the jewels were around her neck and she went down to join the dinner.

The next day at four o'clock she married Tom Buchanan. Soon after that they began a trip to the South Seas for three months.

I saw them after they came back, and I had never seen a girl so happy about her husband. If he left the room for even a minute she'd ask, "Where's Tom?" and she would look nervous until he returned. She would often sit on the beach with his head on her knees. She would put her fingers over his eyes and look at him with the deepest happiness. That was in August. A week later I left Santa Barbara and Tom had a car accident. I read about it in the newspapers. There was a girl with him in the car during the accident — she was a worker at the Santa Barbara hotel. That was Tom's first secret love *affair* with other girls.

Eight months later Daisy had her baby, and they went to live in France for a year or two. After that they came back to live in Chicago. They spent their time with a wild group of the young and rich people, but Daisy didn't drink and never *got into any trouble*. Not drinking among hard-drinking people is a great advantage.

但她不再提那封信了。我们给她洗澡，把冰放到她头上，给她又穿上礼服。半小时后她脖子上带着珠宝项链，下来吃晚餐。

第二天四点钟时她和汤姆·布坎南结婚了，那之后不久他们开始了为期三个月的南太平洋之旅。

他们回来后，我去看他们，我从来没见过一个女孩对她丈夫如此满意。如果他离开屋子哪怕是一小会儿，她都会问，"汤姆去哪儿了?"她看上去惶惶不安，直到他回来为止。她经常坐在海边，汤姆的头枕在她的膝盖上。她用手指罩住他的眼睛，欣喜若狂地看着他。那是在八月份。我离开圣巴巴拉一个星期后，汤姆遭遇了一场车祸。我是从报纸上看到这条消息的。事故发生时有个女孩也在他车里，她是圣巴巴拉旅馆的一名工人。那是汤姆第一次和别的姑娘有秘密私情。

八个月后黛西生了个孩子，他们去法国住了一两年，然后他们又回到芝加哥住。他们与一大群放荡的年轻富人泡在一起，但黛西不喝酒，从没惹什么麻烦。在一群嗜酒如命的人里边滴酒不沾是大有裨益的。

affair [ə'feə] *n.* 恋爱事件；（有指关系不长久的）风流韵事；私通。a love affair 恋爱事件。have an affair with sb. 与某人发生暧昧关系。
get sb. into trouble（使某人）陷入困境、招致麻烦。例如：You'll get into trouble. 你会倒霉的。口语中还可委婉表示"（使某人）未婚先孕"。例如：He's got a girl into trouble. 他已使一个姑娘未婚先孕。

91

Then, six weeks ago, she heard us talking about Gatsby. She had not heard that name for many years. After you left she came into my room and asked me, "Can you describe this Gatsby?" When I described him, she looked shocked. Then she said in the strangest voice that he must be the man she used to know. Then I remembered about the man that was with her in her white car.

When Jordan finished telling me this story we left the hotel and went driving in a carriage through the park.

"It was an amazing chance that brought him so close to her," I said.

"It wasn't an amazing chance at all."

"Why not?"

"Because Gatsby bought that house so that he would be close to Daisy."

I remembered the first time that I saw Gatsby. He was staring out across the water. He must have been looking at Daisy's house. Suddenly I realized that Gatsby was a man with deep feelings and real sadness.

"Gatsby wants your help," said Jordan, "he wants you to invite Daisy to your house for tea and then let him come over."

I was surprised that he wanted so little. He had waited five years and bought a huge house near Daisy. He did all of this just so that he could just "come over" to his neighbor's

后来，也就是六周前，她听我们谈起盖茨比。她好多年没听到这个名字了。你走后，她进我屋问我："你能描述一下这个盖茨比是什么样吗？"当我描述他时，她好像很吃惊。然后她用最奇怪的声调说他一定是她过去认识的那个人。我那时才记起和她一起呆在白色汽车里的那个男子。

乔丹给我讲完故事后，我们离开了旅馆，乘着马车穿过公园。

"这是一个离奇的巧合，使得他离她那么近。"我说。

"可这根本不是什么离奇的巧合。"

"为什么？"

"因为盖茨比买那套房子的目的就是接近黛西。"

我想起了第一次看到盖茨比的情景，他正出神地盯着海水对面。他一定是在看黛西的房子。突然间我意识到盖茨比是一个既有深挚情感又有真切忧伤的人。

"盖茨比需要你的帮助，"乔丹说，"他想让你邀请黛西到你家喝茶，然后再让他过去。"

我很吃惊他的要求竟是如此微不足道。他等了五年，并在黛西附近买了一套大房子，他做这一切只是为了有一天能"来到"他的邻

house one day and see her!

"Why didn't he ask you to help? Couldn't you also arrange a meeting?"

"He wants Daisy to see his house," she said. "I think he had expected her to come to one of his parties, but she never did. So he began asking people if they knew her, and I was the first person he found."

"Do you think that Daisy wants to see Gatsby?" I asked.

"She must not know. You should just invite her to tea."

It was now dark and I put my arm around Jordan's neck and pulled her towards me. I looked into her eyes and asked if she would *join* me for dinner.

Suddenly I stopped thinking about Daisy and Gatsby. I put both my arms around Jordan and her little, scolding mouth smiled. I pulled her closer, this time up to my face.

居家里看她!

"他为什么不要你帮忙?难道你也不能安排一次会面吗?"

"他想要黛西看他的房子,"她说。"我想他原希望她能来参加他的一次聚会,但她从未来过。因此他开始问别人是否认识她,我就是他找到的第一个人。"

"你认为黛西想见盖茨比吗?"我问。

"一定不能让她知道。你应该只邀她来喝茶。"

现在天已经黑了,我搂住乔丹的脖子把她拉过来。我注视着她的眼睛,问她是否愿意和我一块吃晚饭。

我忽然不再想黛西和盖茨比了。我双手搂住乔丹,她那小巧而且流露着嘲讽表情的嘴笑了。我把她拉得更近了,这一次是一直贴到我的脸上。

join [dʒɔin] *vt.* 与…一起做同样一件事、和…做伴。例如:They joined us for lunch. 他们和我们一起吃午饭。

95

CHAPTER FIVE A Tea Party

I came home to West Egg at two in the morning. Light from Gatsby's house was shining all over my yard. At first I thought that Gatsby was having another party, but I couldn't hear any sound. As my taxi drove away I saw Gatsby walking silently towards me across his huge yard.

"Your house looks like a dance hall," I said.

Gatsby turned his eyes towards his house. "I've been looking into some of my rooms. Let's *have a bathe* in the swimming pool, eh, young fellow? I still haven't used my pool all summer."

"Sorry," I said. "I have to work tomorrow. I should go to bed."

"I understand." He waited, *staring at* me eagerly.

"Well, I talked with Jordan Baker," I said after a moment. "I'll call up Daisy tomorrow. I'll invite her over here to tea soon."

"That's all right," he carelessly said. "I don't want to trouble you."

"What day would be best for you?"

"What day would be best for you?" he quickly corrected me.

"Is the day after tomorrow okay, at four-thirty?"

He thought for a moment, and then said, "First I want to

第五章 一次茶会

凌晨两点钟我回到在西卵镇的家。盖茨比家的灯光照亮了我家的整个院子。开始我以为盖茨比家又在聚会了，但听不到任何声响。我坐的出租车走后，我看见盖茨比正穿过他家的大院子默默地向我走来。

"你的房子像个舞厅，"我说。

盖茨比把眼睛转向他的房子。"我刚才一直在随便查看几间屋子。我们在游泳池里游会儿泳，怎么样，老兄?整个夏天我还没用过我的游泳池呢。"

"对不起，"我说。"我明天得上班。我该睡觉了。"

"我明白。"他等着并急切地看着我。

"哦，我跟乔丹·贝克谈了，"过了一会儿我说。"我明天给黛西打电话。我会尽快邀她过来喝茶的。"

"那好，"他心不在焉地说。"我不想麻烦你。"

"你觉得最好是哪一天?"

"你觉得哪天最好?"他很快更正我。

"后天可以吗，四点半?"

他想了一会儿，然后说，"我想先请人

have a bathe（为游乐或取凉而）游泳。bathe 游泳，尤指海（或河、湖）水浴。

stare at sb. 盯着某人看。stare at sb. in horror 恐惧地盯着某人看；stare at sb. in open-mouthed wonder目瞪口呆。

97

have the grass cut."

We both looked down at the yard — there was a clear line where my untidy yard ended and his tidy yard began. I knew that he meant my grass.

"There's another matter." He paused for a second. "I thought ... young fellow, you don't make a lot of money, do you?"

"No, not very much."

"I thought you didn't. I don't want to say anything rude, but ... I have a small business, very small, you understand. And I thought maybe — if you don't make much money — you are selling bonds, aren't you, young fellow?"

"I'm trying to."

"Well, I think this would *interest* you. It wouldn't use too much of your time and you would earn a good bit of money."

In a different situation, this conversation could have changed my whole life. But I knew that he offered me this opportunity only to repay me for my help — so I couldn't accept it.

"Sorry, but I'm too busy," I said. "Thanks very much, but I don't have time to do any more work."

The next morning I *called up* Daisy, and invited her to come over for tea. I told her not to bring Tom.

The next day I waited for her to come over. It was raining heavily outside. At noon a man wearing a raincoat knocked at my door and said that Mr. Gatsby had hired him to cut my grass. I remembered then that I needed to go into town to buy some

把草坪修剪修剪。"

我们都低头看院子——在我家乱糟糟的院子和他家整洁的院子接头处，有一条明显的界线，我知道他指的是我家的草坪。

"还有件事。"他停了一下。"我原想……老兄，你挣钱不多，是吗？"

"是的，不太多。"

"我想你赚钱不多。我不想说什么无礼的话，但……我做了一项小生意，非常小，你知道的。我想也许——如果你挣钱不多——你在卖债券，是不是，老兄？"

"试着干呗。"

"好，我想这会让你感兴趣。无需花费太多时间，你就能挣很多钱。"

换一种情形，这个谈话也许会改变我的一生。但我知道他提供这个机会只是想报答我的帮助——因此我不能接受。

"对不起，可是我太忙了，"我说。"非常感谢，但我没有时间去做更多的工作了。"

第二天早晨我打电话给黛西，邀请她过来喝茶，并告诉她不要带汤姆来。

第二天我等她过来。外面下着大雨，中午有个人穿着雨衣敲我家的门，说盖茨比先生雇他为我家修剪草地。这时我才想起我需要去镇上买些柠檬和鲜花。

interest ['intrist] ***vt.*** 使感兴趣；引起…的关注。interest children in reading 使孩子们对读书产生兴趣。
call up <美>打电话或打电话给。例如：Someone called up from downtown and asked to see you at five. 有人从市里打电话来，要求在5点钟来看你。后面可跟接电话的人，如：Call up Xiao Wang, please. 请给小王打电话。

99

lemons and flowers.

Later I saw that the flowers were not necessary, for at three o'clock one of Gatsby's servants brought over a great pile of flowers. Almost an hour later my front door was opened nervously, and Gatsby, wearing a white suit, a silver shirt, and a gold-colored tie, hurried inside. His face was pale white, and there was darkness under his eyes. I knew that he had not slept well.

"Is everything all right?" he asked me at once.

"The grass looks good, if that's what you mean."

"What grass?" he asked. "Oh, the grass in the yard, yes." He looked out of the window at it, but he was *too* nervous *to* really see anything. "Do you have everything that you need — enough tea?"

I *took him into* my kitchen and showed him the twelve lemon cakes I bought from the village shop.

"Is this enough?" I asked.

"Of course, of course! They're just fine!"

He sat down in the living room and stared at the window. He then began turning the pages of one of my books nervously. Every few moments he looked towards the window. Finally he stood up and told me, in a terribly sad voice, that he was going home.

"Why?" I asked him.

"It's too late! Nobody's coming to tea."

后来我发现鲜花是多余的，因为三点钟时盖茨比的一个仆人送来一大堆鲜花。大约一小时后我的前门战战兢兢地开了，盖茨比，穿着一身白色西装，银色衬衫，打着金色领带，慌慌张张地走了进来。脸色发白，眼睛下方有道道黑晕。我知道他没睡好。

"都准备好了吗?"他马上问。

"草坪看上去还不错，如果你指的是这个的话。"

"什么草坪?"他问。"噢，对了，院里的草坪。"他透过窗子朝那儿望去，但他太紧张了，实际上什么也没看见。"所需要的东西你都弄够了吗?——茶点够吗?"

我把他领进厨房，给他看从村上店铺里买来的十二钟柠檬蛋糕。

"够吗?"我问。

"当然，当然!正好!"

他坐在客厅里，眼睛盯着窗子，然后又开始紧张地一页页翻弄我的一本书。每隔一小会儿他就朝窗户望一下。最后他站起来，用极忧伤的音调告诉我，他要回家了。

"为什么?"我问他。

"太晚了!没人要来喝茶啦。"

too... to... 太…以致不能…。
例如：It is too early to announce. 现在宣布为时过早。
take sb. into 将某人带入…里面

101

"Don't be silly; it's just now two minutes to four."

At that moment we heard the sound of a car coming towards my house. I walked out into the yard and saw the Buchanans' large car coming up. The driver stopped, and Daisy's face looked out at me with a wide smile.

"Is this really where you live, my wonderful cousin?"

Her voice sounded like music and was as exciting as ever. "*Are* you *in love with* me," she whispered softly in my ear, "why did I have to come here alone?"

"That's my secret." I said. "Tell your driver to go far away and wait an hour."

We went inside. To my surprise, the living room was now empty.

Then we heard a light knock at the back door. I went and opened it. Gatsby was standing there, pale as death. He was staring into my eyes like he was in great pain. He walked by me into the living room.

For a minute there wasn't any sound. I could feel my own heart jumping in my chest. Finally I heard Daisy's clear voice.

"I truly am glad to see you again."

I had nothing to do in the hall, so I went to join them in the living room.

Gatsby was standing next to the fireplace and Daisy was sitting on the opposite side of the room in a hard chair. Neither of them was speaking.

"别傻了；现在刚刚三点五十八分。"

就在那时我们听到汽车朝我家开过来的声音。我出门进了院子，看到布坎南的大汽车开过来。司机停下车，黛西一脸欢笑地朝外看着我。

"我了不起的表哥，这真是你住的地方吗？"

她的声音像音乐一样好听，也一如既往地撩人心弦。"你是不是爱上我了？"她附在我耳边轻声说，"为什么非要我单独来这儿？"

"这是我的秘密。"我说。"叫你的司机走得远远的等一个小时。"

我们走进去。让我吃惊的是，客厅里此时已空无一人。

然后我们听到后门有轻轻的敲门声，我过去开了门，盖茨比站在那儿，面如死灰。他盯着我的眼睛，好像非常痛苦。他随我走进客厅。

有一分钟没有一点儿动静。我能感觉到自己的心跳。最后我听到黛西清晰的声音。

"我真高兴又见到你。"

在大厅里我无事可做，因此我走进客厅，和他们在一起。

盖茨比站在壁炉旁，黛西坐在对面一张硬座椅子上。两人都没说话。

be in love with sb. 热恋着。如：I'm in love with music. 我热爱音乐。

103

"We've met before," said Gatsby in a low voice.

"We haven't met for many years," said Daisy without any feeling in her voice.

"It has been more than four years *since* we saw each other," said Gatsby and there was a long silence.

I then poured some tea, and we all drank tea and ate lemon cakes. Daisy and I began to talk, and Gatsby looked at us with unhappy eyes. After talking for a little while I said that I had to make a phone call and stood up.

"Who are you calling?" demanded Gatsby nervously.

"I'll be back in a minute." I said.

"I need to speak to you for a moment before you go." He followed me wildly into the kitchen, quickly closed the door, and whispered "Oh God!" in a terrible way.

"What's wrong?" I asked.

"This is a terrible mistake," he said, *shaking his head from side to side*. "A truly terrible mistake."

"You're just embarrassed, that's all," and luckily I also said, "Daisy is embarrassed also."

"She's also embarrassed?" he repeated in shock.

"Just as much as you are."

"Don't speak so loudly." He whispered.

"You're acting like a little child," I said. " Not only that, but you're also being rude. Daisy is sitting there all alone."

"我们以前见过面，"盖茨比低声说。

"我们好多年没见面了，"黛西的声音里毫无感情。

"从上次见面以来我们已经有四年多没见面了，"盖茨比说，然后是一阵长时间的沉默。

这时我开始倒茶，然后我们喝着茶，吃着柠檬蛋糕。黛西和我开始说话，盖茨比用郁郁不乐的眼神看着我们。谈了一小会儿后我说我得打个电话，就站了起来。

"你给谁打电话？"盖茨比紧张地问。

"我马上回来。"我说。

"你走之前，我需要跟你谈一会儿。"他急切地跟着我走进厨房，很快关上门，低声说："啊，上帝！"样子很可怕。

"怎么啦？"我问。

"这是个可怕的错误，"他摇着头说，"一个真正可怕的错误。"

"你只是拘谨罢了，就这么回事，"幸好我又说了一句："黛西也拘谨。"

"她也拘谨？"他吃惊地重复道。

"就跟你一样拘谨。"

"别说这么大声。"他低语道。

"你就像一个小孩，"我说。"不仅如此，你还有些失礼，黛西就一个人坐在那儿呢。"

---

since [sins] *conj.* 自…以来，从…以后。多用于完成时态。如：It's been years since I enjoyed myself so much as last night. 我已经有很多年没有像昨天晚上那样痛快了。since还常有"因为、既然"之义。例如：Since it is late I shall go home now. 因为天晚了，我现在要回家了。

shake one's head from side to side 摇头。from side to side从一边到另一边，从左到右。相似词组还有side by side 肩并肩地；同等地。from time to time 时时，间或。

He raised his hand up to stop my words, gave me a sad and afraid look, and went back into the living room.

I walked out the back door, just as Gatsby had done before. I closed the door with a loud sound so that Gatsby and Daisy would know that I had left. It was raining hard again, and I ran under a huge black tree in the yard. Its thick leaves stopped some of the rain. There was nothing to look at around the tree except Gatsby's huge house, so I stared up at it for half an hour.

Then the sun began to shine again, and I felt it was a good time to go back inside. I went in — and made every possible noise that I could in the kitchen so that they would know I was back — but I don't believe they heard a sound. When I went back in they were both sitting on the sofa, looking at each other, and all of their embarrassment from before was gone. Daisy's face was covered with soft tears, and when I came in she began to clean it with her handkerchief. The change in Gatsby was simply amazing — his happiness shone from him and filled the little room.

"Hello, young fellow," he said, as if he hadn't seen me for many years.

"It's stopped raining." I said.

"Oh, has it?" When he understood what I was talking about he smiled and repeated the good news to Daisy. " What do you think of that, Daisy? It's stopped raining."

他抬起手不让我再说了，神情忧伤而害怕地看了我一眼，又走回客厅。

我从后门走了出去，就像先前盖茨比一样。我把门关得很响，好让盖茨比和黛西知道我已经走了。雨下得又大了起来，我跑到院子里一棵黑色的大树下。浓密的树叶挡住了些雨。除了盖茨比的大房子之外，树四周也没什么可看的，因此我只好抬头盯着它瞧了半个小时。

后来阳光又开始照射了，我觉得是回屋的时候了。我走进去——在厨房里尽量弄出声响，好让他们知道我回来了——但我相信他们什么也没听见。我走进去时他们都坐在沙发上，互相看着，先前所有的拘谨都已荡然无存。黛西的脸上满是泪滴，我进去时，她开始用手绢擦。盖茨比的变化简直令人吃惊——幸福从他身上闪耀出来，洋溢于整个小屋之中。

"你好，老兄，"他说，就好像许多年没见过我一样。

"雨停了。"我说。

"噢，是吗？"他明白过来我说的话后，笑着对黛西重复这个好消息。"你觉得怎么样，黛西？雨停了。"

"I'm glad, Jay."

"Would you and Daisy come over to my house?" he asked.   "I'd like her to see it."

Gatsby and I waited in the garden, while Daisy went upstairs to wash her face.

"My house looks great, doesn't it?" he demanded.

I agreed that it was very fancy.

His eyes looked over it, every door and wall.

"It only took me three years to earn the money to buy it."

"I thought you got your money from your father."

"I did, young fellow, but I lost most of it during the war."

I don't think he knew what he was saying, for when I asked him what business he did he answered,   "That's my private affair,"   before he realized that it was not a polite answer.

"I've done many things,"   he corrected himself.   "First I *was in the medicine business* and then I was in the oil business."

Just then Daisy came out of the house.

"That huge place there?"   she cried, pointing.

"Yes, do you like it?"

"I love it, but I don't understand how you can live there all alone."

"I always keep it full of interesting people, night and day: interesting people and famous people."

"我很高兴，杰伊。"

"你愿意和黛西去我家吗？"他问。"我想让她去看看。"

黛西上楼去洗脸，而我和盖茨比在花园里等着。

"我的房子看上去很棒，是不是？"他问。

我赞同说那房子很别致。

他的眼睛扫过整个房子，扫过每一扇门，每一堵墙。

"我只花了三年时间挣钱买这套房子。"

"我还以为你是从你父亲那儿继承的钱。"

"我是继承了钱，老兄，可是战争期间丢了一大半。"

我觉得他不知道自己在说什么，因为当我问他做什么生意时，他却回答："这是私事"，然后才意识到这样回答不礼貌。

"我做过好多生意，"他改了口。"首先是做医药生意，然后从事过石油业。"

就在这时，黛西从屋里走了出来。

"就是那边那座大房子吗？"她大声说，手还指点着。

"是的，喜欢吗？"

"喜欢，但我不明白你怎么能独自一人住在那儿。"

"我让那里无论昼夜总是充满有趣的人，有趣的人和知名的人。"

be in the medicine business

意为"经营药品生意"。in business 经商、经营；开始工作。例如：The 15-member committee is expected to be in business by early June. 15 人组成的委员会可望于6月初开始活动。

Instead of walking straight across the garden, we walked down the road and entered through the gate. Daisy admired the house standing dark *against* the bright sky; she admired the gardens, sweet-smelling flowers.

It was strange to go into Gatsby's house when it was so quiet. There was no movement inside. No bright dresses and no sounds but the birds in the trees. As we walked through the huge rooms, I felt that there were guests hiding behind every sofa and table, who were all ordered to be silent until we had passed through the room.

We went upstairs, through many bedrooms full of fresh flowers, through many halls and bathrooms. We went into one room where a young man was exercising on the floor. His name was Mr. Klipspringer, and he was living in the house as Gatsby's guest. Finally we arrived at Gatsby's own private rooms, a large bedroom, a bathroom and a study. We sat down in the study and drank a glass of some wine he took from a cupboard.

This whole time he hadn't once stopped looking at Daisy. Once he was looking at her so closely that he almost fell down the stairs.

His bedroom was the simplest room in the house — except that on the table was a brush and comb set made of pure gold. Daisy grasped the brush with great happiness, and put it to her hair. Gatsby sat down and began to laugh happily. I had never seen him so happy.

我们没有直接穿过花园，而是沿着大路走进大门。在明净的天空的映衬下矗立着的房子显得黑糊糊的，黛西对此赞赏不已；她还很喜欢花园及里面芬芳的花朵。

走进盖茨比的家竟如此安静，令人奇怪里面毫无响动。没有鲜艳的礼服，除了树上的鸟鸣没有一点儿声音。我们穿过那些大房间时，我觉得每张沙发和桌子后面都藏有客人，他们被命令不许出声，直到我们走过为止。

我们上了楼，穿过一间间摆满鲜花的卧室，穿过一间间大厅和浴室。我们来到一间屋子，屋里有一个年轻人正在地板上训练。他是克利普斯普林格先生，盖茨比的客人，住在大宅里。最后我们来到盖茨比的私人房间，有一间大卧室、一个洗澡间和一间书房。我们坐在书房里，喝着一杯他从橱柜里拿出来的一种酒。

整个这段时间他一刻不停地看着黛西。曾有一次他看她时离得那么近，以致于差点儿跌下楼梯。

他的卧室是房子里最简朴的——除了桌子上放着一套纯金梳妆用具。黛西极其高兴地抓起发刷，放到自己的头上。盖茨比坐下来，开始开心地笑着。我从没见过他如此开心。

against [ə'genst] *prep*. 这里意为 "以…为背景；和…对照；以…衬托"。如：The ship appeared against the sky. 在天水间出现了船只。

"It's the funniest thing, young fellow," he said. "I can't — When I try to — "

Gatsby could not speak. He had *moved* through two kinds of emotion and was now beginning a third. The first emotion was embarrassment and the second was joy; now he was simply amazed that Daisy was real and that she was really standing so close to him. He had been dreaming of her for so many years. Now the waiting was finally over.

He then opened two large cupboards which were full of his suits and ties, and his many shirts, sitting in several high piles.

"I have a man in England who buys me clothes. He sends over what he has found at the beginning of each season."

He took out a pile of beautiful shirts and began throwing them, one by one, in front of us — some were made of fine cotton and others were thick silk. They soon covered the table with their many colors. While we admired them he pulled out more, and the pile grew higher and higher. Suddenly Daisy put her head into the shirts and began to cry wildly.

"They're all such beautiful shirts," she cried. "It makes me so sad because I've never seen shirts like these before."

After seeing the house, we were going to see the gardens and the flowers and the swimming pool and the sea-plane — but it began to rain again outside, so we stood near the window and looked at the ocean.

"这是最让人高兴的事，老兄，"他说。"我不能——我想到要——"

盖茨比说不出话来。他已经经历了两种情感，目前正进入第三种。第一种是窘迫不安，第二种是欣喜若狂，而现在他简直不敢相信黛西是真的，她真的站得离他这么近。他多年来一直梦绕魂牵着她。如今等待终于结束了。

接着，他打开两个大橱柜，里面装满了西装、领带和许多衬衫，叠成高高的几摞。

"有个人在英国为我买衣服，他在每个季初挑好了衣服送过来。"

他拿出了一摞漂亮的衬衫，开始一件一件地扔到我们面前——有的是精梳棉的，有的是厚绸的。很快桌子上堆满了各色衣服。我们欣赏着，他又拽出更多的衣服，衣服堆得越来越高。突然黛西一头扎进衣堆里不顾一切地哭了起来。

"这是些多么漂亮的衣服啊，"她哭道，"这让我太伤心了，因为我以前从没见过这样的衬衫。"

看完房子，我们准备去看花园、鲜花、游泳池和水上飞机——但是外面又开始下起雨来，我们只好站在窗边看着大海。

move [muːv] *vi.* 表示"事情等进展"。

113

"If it wasn't for the thick mist we could see your house across the water," said Gatsby. "Every night you always have a green light that sits at the end of your wall."

Gatsby seemed to be thinking. Perhaps he realized that the importance of that light was now gone. Before, when he was *separated from* Daisy by a great distance, the light had seemed very near to her, almost next to her. It looked as close as a star was to the moon. Now it was just a common green light on a wall.

I began to walk around the room and look at Gatsby's things. A large photograph of an old man in sailing clothes interested me.

"Who is this?" I asked.

"That? Oh, that's Mr. Dan Cody, young fellow. He's dead now. He used to be my best friend many years ago."

"Come here quickly!" cried Daisy at the window.

The rain was still falling, but in the west pink clouds moved slowly over the sea.

"Look at those clouds," she whispered to Gatsby. "I'd like to put you in one of those pink clouds and push you around."

When I heard them whispering like young lovers I tried to go home, but they wouldn't let me.

"I know what we can do," said Gatsby, "we'll have Mr. Klipspringer play the piano."

"如果不是因为这浓雾，我们就可以看到大海对面你的家了。"盖茨比说，"在你那边海堤的尽头，每晚你都点着一盏绿灯。"

盖茨比好像在沉思。也许他意识到那盏灯现在已不重要了。以前他和黛西被一大段距离隔开时，那盏灯似乎离她很近，几乎就在旁边，就像一颗星星离月亮那样近。此时它只不过是堤上一盏普通的绿灯。

我开始在屋里走走，看看盖茨比的东西。一张大照片引起了我的注意，照片上是一个穿着航海服的老人。

"这是谁呀?"我问。

"那个吗?哦，老兄，那是丹·科迪先生。现在他已经死了。很多年前他曾是我最好的朋友。"

"快过来!"黛西在窗边大声喊。

雨还在下，但在西边，粉红色的云缓缓地飘在大海上。

"看那些云，"她低声对盖茨比说。"我想把你放到一朵粉红色的云彩里，推着你四处转悠。"

当我听到他们像年轻的恋人一样悄悄低语时，我就想要回家，但他们不让我走。

"我知道我们可以干什么，"盖茨比说，"我们让克利普斯普林格先生弹钢琴。"

separate sb. from sb. "把…和…分开"。如：The school separates boys from girls. 学校把男生与女生分开。

He went out of the room and returned with the young man, who looked embarrassed.

"I don't play the piano well," he said. "I don't — hardly play at all. I haven't practiced for a long time."

"We'll go downstairs to the music room," interrupted Gatsby.

In the music room Gatsby turned on a lamp beside the piano, the rest of the room was dark and private. He lit Daisy's cigarette and sat down with her on the sofa in the darkest corner of the room.

Klipspringer played the old song "The Love Nest". After he finished he turned around unhappily.

"You see, I'm not good at playing, I told you I haven't practiced — "

"Don't talk so much, young fellow," ordered Gatsby. "Play!"

He played.

Outside the wind was blowing loud. All the lights in West Egg were going on now. It was time for me to go home.

As I said goodbye, I saw fear and doubt on Gatsby's face. It looked like he *was* not *sure about* his new happiness. For five years he had been dreaming of Daisy. During that time he had been building a dream of Daisy. Now they were in the same room together. How could any real person be as good as the dream? There must have been some moments that afternoon

他走出屋子然后带来那个年轻人，那个年轻人看上去有些拘谨。

"我弹得不好，"他说。"我不——几乎根本不弹，我还没练多长时间。"

"我们都去楼下音乐厅，"盖茨比打断他的话。

在音乐厅，盖茨比打开钢琴旁边的一盏灯，屋子里的其余部分又黑又隐秘。他为黛西点着一支烟，然后与她坐在屋子最黑暗一角的沙发上。

克利普斯普林格演奏的是老歌"爱之巢"，演奏完后他不高兴地转过身来。

"你们看，我不擅长弹奏，我告诉你们了，我还没练——"

"别说那么多，老兄，"盖茨比命令道。"弹奏！"

他弹了起来。

屋外风正猛烈地吹着。现在西卵镇所有的灯都亮了，我该回家了。

道别时，我看见盖茨比脸上有一种恐惧和疑虑的表情，好像他对新的幸福没有把握。五年了，他一直在梦想着黛西。那些时间里他一直在构筑关于黛西的梦想，此刻他们一块儿待在一个屋子里。真实的人能和梦境中的一样美吗?那天下午肯定有过一些时候，黛西让他失望了。

be sure about "确信…" "有把握…" "自信…"。例如:
I could not feel sure about it.
对这件事我没有把握。

117

when Daisy had disappointed him.

As I *watched* him his face again became happy. His hand grasped hers, and when she whispered something quietly in his ear he turned towards her showing a deep feeling in his face. Her voice had a magic power that was better than a dream.

They had forgotten me now, but Daisy looked up and raised her hand to say goodbye; Gatsby didn't know me now at all. I left the room and walked downstairs into the rain and left them there together.

我看他时，他脸色又变得高兴起来。他抓着她的手，当她轻声在他耳边说话时，他深情款款地转向她。她的声音里有一种比梦还美妙的魔力。

他们此刻已经忘记了我的存在，但黛西抬起头，举手跟我道别；盖茨比此时根本都不知道我了。我离开屋子下了台阶走进雨中，留下他们俩待在一起。

---

watch [wɔtʃ] *vt.*注视，留神观察，观看。如：Watch that boy jump.注意观察那个男孩跳。

CHAPTER SIX The Big Party

All summer Gatsby's fame was increasing, but it was not a good kind of fame. The hundreds of people who had attended his many parties were all telling different stories about his past — none of the stories were true.

I did not believe the stories about him. I didn't learn his true story of his life *until* much later, when he told it to me with his own mouth. But I will tell it to you now, to stop all of the untrue ideas.

His real name wasn't Mr. Jay Gatsby. His real name was James Gatz, and he was born in North Dakota. His family was poor farmers and had never been very successful — *in his heart* he had never truly believed that they were his real parents. *In his mind* he was a completely different person. Every night as he lay down in his bed he felt troubled. His mind filled with strange thoughts and dreams of an amazing and beautiful world — it was a world much better than his. But a man like James Gatz was too common to live in this amazing and beautiful world. To go to this world he needed a new name — he needed to become a new person. When he was only seventeen he invented Jay Gatsby, and this Jay Gatsby was *the kind of* person that he wanted to be. Every day he worked to change himself into Jay Gatsby.

Gatz's new life began when he saw a huge boat out on

第六章 大型聚会

整个夏天，盖茨比的名气不断增大，但都不是些好名声。几百个多次参加过他的聚会的人都在讲与他过去有关的各种不同的故事——但没有一个是真的。

我不相信那些关于他的故事。直到很久以后，我才了解到他的真实故事，那是他亲口告诉我的。但我现在要讲给你们听，以止住所有不真实的看法。

他的真名不叫杰伊·盖茨比先生。他真名叫詹姆斯·盖茨，出生在北达科他州。他父母是贫穷的农民，从来都没什么成就——从他的内心讲，他从来都没有真正相信过他们是他的亲生父母。在他的心中，自己是个截然不同的人。每天夜晚当他躺到床上时就觉得苦恼。他的头脑里充满了各种奇特的念头和对奇异而美丽的世界的梦想——那是一个比他现实拥有的要美好得多的世界。但是像詹姆斯·盖茨这样的人太普通了，不能生活在这个奇异而美丽的世界中。为了进入这个世界他需要一个新名字——他需要变成一个新人。他只有十七岁时，杜撰出了一个杰伊·盖茨比，这个杰伊·盖茨比就是他想变成的那种人。每天他都努力把自己改变成杰伊·盖茨比。

当盖茨看见一艘大船在苏必利尔湖上航

until [ʌn'til] *prep.* "直到…时候；到…为止"。例如：It was cold from November until April. 天气从11月份一直冷到4月份。"（用于否定句）在…之前；直到…才"。例如：He didn't go until midnight. 他直到午夜才走。

in one's heart 在内心、在感情深处

in one's mind 在头脑里、在思想里

the kind of sb. "这样一种人"。如：He is not the kind of man to idle away his time. 他不是那种游手好闲的人。

Lake Superior. The boat belonged to Dan Cody, the man in the picture in Gatsby's bedroom. For the last year Gatz had been working on Lake Superior, catching fish or doing anything that would give him enough money for food and a bed. He was still looking for some work to do on the day that Dan Cody's boat sailed close to him. It was a fancy and beautiful boat. As Gatz was walking along the shore he saw it stop in a dangerous area just a little distance from the shore. So he borrowed a little boat, rowed it out to the Cody's sailing boat and told Cody that a strong wind might come soon and break the boat on the rocks.

Cody thanked Gatz and asked him his name, James Gatz answered, " Jay Gatsby."

At that time Cody was fifty years old, and very *rich from* his many gold and silver mines in Mexico. Cody's body was still strong, but his mind was weak. Many women knew this and tried to marry him for his money. One of these women was Ella Kaye, a famous newspaper woman. Cody had been living on his boat for five years; he was sailing around the world, when James Gatz saw him.

James Gatz felt that the sailing boat represented all the wealth and beauty in the world.

Cody asked him some questions and learned that Gatsby was smart and very determined, so he decided to hire him. Just a few days later he bought a blue coat, five pairs of white

行时，他的新生活开始了。这艘船是丹·科迪的，就是盖茨比卧室里照片上的那个人。前一年盖茨一直在苏必利尔湖上干活，捕鱼或干那些凡是能够赚钱为自己换来食宿的事儿。在丹·科迪的船开近他的那天他仍旧在找活儿干。这是一艘光彩夺目的漂亮大船。当盖茨在沿岸边走着时，他看见大船正停在离岸很近的一个危险地带。于是他借了一条小船，划到科迪的帆船边，告诉科迪大风可能很快就会来把船撞毁到礁石上。

科迪很感谢盖茨，并问了他的名字。杰姆斯·盖茨回答说："杰伊·盖茨比。"

那时科迪已经五十岁了，在墨西哥有很多金矿和银矿，因此非常富裕。科迪的身体仍很强壮，脑子却不大好使。许多女人都知道这一点，为了钱都想办法嫁给他。其中一个女人叫埃拉·凯，是一位著名的女记者。当杰姆斯·盖茨看见他时，他已经在船上呆了五年了，一直在世界各地转悠。

杰姆斯·盖茨觉得那艘帆船象征着世界上所有的财富和美丽。

科迪问了他一些问题，了解到盖茨比聪明伶俐且颇有雄心壮志，于是决定雇用他。几天后，他给盖茨比买来一件蓝上衣、五条白裤

rich from 靠⋯富有。如：Grow rich from writing novels. 因写小说致富。

123

trousers and a white sailing hat for Gatsby. And when his boat left for North Africa, Gatsby went with him. He helped sail the boat, worked as Cody's secretary, and even had to help Cody eat sometimes. For when Dan Cody was drunk he was *no better than* a baby. This situation lasted a few years, and during this time the boat traveled around America three times. Then one night in New York, Ella Kaye came onto the boat, and a week later Dan Cody died.

Cody loved wine and women too much — especially wine. That was the reason Gatsby drank so little.

When Cody died he left some money — thirty thousand dollars — to Gatsby. But Gatsby never received the money. Ella Kaye, using the help of a clever lawyer, took all of Cody's money.

For many weeks after my *little tea party for* Daisy, I didn't see Gatsby. During this time I was often in New York City, walking around and talking with Jordan. But finally I decided to go over to Gatsby's house one Saturday afternoon. I'd sat there with him for only about two minutes when somebody brought Tom Buchanan in for a drink. There were three of them together, all riding horses — Tom, a man named Sloana and a pretty woman who I had seen there before. I was surprised to see Tom in Gatsby's house, of course, but the really surprising thing was that Tom lived so close and had never come over before.

子和一顶白色的航海帽。当船开往北非时，盖茨比就跟着他了。他帮着开船，给科迪做秘书，甚至有时还得给科迪喂饭，因为丹·科迪喝醉时简直就是一个小孩儿。这种情形持续了几年，在这期间船绕美洲航行了三次。接下来在纽约的一天晚上，埃拉·凯上了船，一周后丹·科迪就死了。

科迪沉溺于酒和女人——尤其是酒。这就是盖茨比很少喝酒的原因。

科迪死时留了一些钱——三万美元——给盖茨比。但盖茨比从来没有拿到这笔钱，埃拉·凯在一个精明律师的帮助下弄走了科迪所有的钱。

在那次请黛西来喝茶后的好多星期，我都没见过盖茨比。这段时间，我经常呆在纽约，和乔丹四处闲逛和聊天。但一个星期六的下午我终于决定去盖茨比家。我和他刚坐了大约两分钟就有人带着汤姆·布坎南进来找点东西喝。他们共有三个人，都骑着马——汤姆、一个叫斯隆的男子和一个以前在那儿见过的漂亮女人。看见汤姆在盖茨比家，我吃了一惊，当然，真正让人惊奇的还是汤姆住这么近而以前却从未来过。

no better than no *adv.*作副词，和形容词或副词比较级连用，意为"并不…些（=not any）"。no better than 并不比…好些。

little tea party for 为…举行的午茶小聚会。

"I'm so happy to see you," said Gatsby. "I'm delighted that you came over. Please, sit down. Would you like a cigarette?" Gatsby walked around the room quickly, *ringing a few bells*, "I'll get you something to drink in just a moment."

Mr. Sloane didn't want to drink anything. "A glass of orange juice?" "No, thanks." "A little wine?" "No." "Some tea?" "Nothing at all, thanks..."

Gatsby then turned to Tom.

"I think we've met somewhere before, Mr. Buchanan."

"Oh, yes," Tom said politely, but he obviously could not remember.

"It was about two weeks ago, in the restaurant in the city."

"Oh, yes, that's right. You were together with Nick."

"I know your wife," said Gatsby, almost fiercely.

"You do?" Tom turned to me. "Do you live near here, Nick?"

"Just next door." I said.

"Really?"

Mr. Sloane didn't say anything, and the woman didn't talk either — until suddenly, after drinking two glasses of wine, she became quite friendly.

"We'll all come to your next party, Mr. Gatsby," she said. "What do you say?"

"Of course, I'd be delighted to see you there."

"很高兴看到你们。"盖茨比说。"你们过来我很高兴，请坐。来支烟？"盖茨比在屋里匆匆忙忙地走来走去，摇了几次铃，"我去给你们弄点儿喝的，很快就来。"

斯隆先生什么也不想喝。"要杯橙汁吗？""不要，谢谢。""来点酒吧？""不要。""茶呢？""什么也不要，谢谢……"

于是盖茨比转向汤姆。

"我想我们以前在哪儿见过面，布坎南先生。"

"哦，是的，"汤姆礼貌地说，但他显然不记得了。

"大概两周前，在城里的一家饭馆。"

"哦，是的，对了。你和尼克在一块儿。"

"我认识你妻子，"盖茨比说，几乎带有攻击性。

"是吗？"汤姆转向我。"尼克，你就住在这附近吗？"

"就在隔壁。"我说。

"真的？"

斯隆先生一句话也没说，那个女人也没说话——直到喝了两杯酒后，她才突然变得非常友好起来。

"盖茨比先生，下一次聚会我们都来，"她说。"您说呢？"

"当然好啦，我很高兴在聚会上见到你们。"

ring a few bells 按了几下铃。

ring *vt.* 敲响钟；按铃。

127

"That would be nice," said Mr. Sloane in a cold voice. "Well — I think we should start going home." He quickly stood up.

"Why don't you stay here for dinner?" said Gatsby, it *seemed like* he wanted to watch Tom more.

"Why don't you come to dinner with me?" said the lady to Gatsby.

"Let's go now," said Mr. Sloane to the woman.

Gatsby wanted to go together with them, but didn't see that Mr. Sloane didn't want him to join. "I don't have a horse," he said. "I know, I'll follow you in my car. Can you wait here for just a minute?"

The rest of us went outside, and Mr. Sloane and the woman walked down the stairs towards their horses.

Tom looked at me angrily and said, "Where did he meet Daisy? I don't *like her going* out alone."

"Let's go, Tom," Mr. Sloane called, "We've got to go. We're late." He then said to me, "Tell Mr. Gatsby we couldn't wait."

They all rode down the road quickly. When Gatsby came out they had already disappeared.

Tom was obviously worried when Daisy went out alone. So, the next Saturday night he came together with her to Gatsby's party. The party that night had a strange and heavy feeling in the air. It was very different from Gatsby's other parties that

"那就好，"斯隆先生冷冷地说。"我说——我想我们该回去了。"他很快站起来。

"为什么不留在这儿吃晚饭"盖茨比说，看样子他是想和汤姆多呆一会儿。

"为何不跟我一块吃晚饭呢?"那女士对盖茨比说。

"我们走吧，"斯隆先生对那个女人说。

盖茨比想跟他们一块儿去，但没注意到斯隆先生不想让他加入。"我没有马，"他说，"我开车跟着你们。能稍等一会儿吗?"

我们其余的人都走出去，斯隆先生和那位女士下了台阶向他们的马走去。

汤姆生气地看着我说，"他在哪儿见到黛西的?我不喜欢黛西一个人出门。"

"走吧，汤姆，"斯隆先生叫道。"我们得走了。已经迟了。"然后他对我说，"告诉盖茨比先生，我们等不及了。"

他们都骑上马沿路迅速地走了，盖茨比出来时他们已经没有踪影了。

汤姆显然很担心黛西一个人外出，因此接下来一个星期六的晚上他和黛西一块儿来参加盖茨比家的聚会。那晚的聚会上气氛奇怪、沉闷，与那个夏天盖茨比的其它聚会有很大不

seem like 看来好像。如：
After what seemed like hours he came out with a wry smile. 好像过了好几个小时，他才出来，脸上挂着苦笑。

like sb. v-ing like 用作动词，可接动名词作宾语，表示"喜爱"，指习惯性动作。例如：
I like taking a walk after supper every day. 每天晚饭后我喜欢散散步。

summer, perhaps because Tom was there. The same people were there, the same wine, the same dancing and other activities, but I felt unhappiness in the air that I had not felt there before.

Tom and Daisy arrived as it became dark, and they walked around the yard with Gatsby and I.

"These parties are so exciting," Daisy whispered to me. "If you want to kiss me during the evening, Nick, just tell me and I'll be happy to arrange it for you."

"Look around the garden," suggested Gatsby.

"I am looking around. I'm having a wonderful time."

"You will see the faces of many famous people."

Tom's scolding eyes looked at the crowd. "I was just thinking that I don't *recognize* anyone here," he said *bitterly*.

"Perhaps you recognize that lady." Gatsby pointed his hand to a woman wearing a fancy red dress; she looked more like a beautiful flower than a young woman. She sat under a tree surrounded by many men. Tom and Daisy stared at her, recognizing that she was a famous movie-star.

"She's so lovely," said Daisy.

"The man standing next to her is her director."

He walked around, introducing us to many people as we went:

"This is Mrs. Buchanan ... and Mr. Buchanan — the polo player."

同，也许是因为汤姆在那儿的缘故吧。还是那些人，同样的酒，同样的舞会和其它活动，但我感觉空气中有种我以前在那从未感觉到的不快。

汤姆和黛西天黑时才到，他们和我、盖茨比在院子里四处走走。

"这些聚会太令人兴奋了，"黛西悄悄对我说。"今晚如果你想吻我，就告诉我好了，我会很高兴为你安排的。"

"看看花园吧，"盖茨比建议道。
"我在往四处看，我玩得很开心。"
"你们可以见到很多有名的人。"
汤姆用挑剔的眼光看着人群。"我只是在想这儿的人我一个也不认识，"他挖苦地说。

"也许你认识那位女士。"盖茨比的手指向一个身穿鲜艳的红礼服的女人；看上去不像是一个年轻女士倒像是一朵美丽的鲜花。她坐在一棵树下，被许多男人们包围着。汤姆和黛西盯着她瞧，认出她是一位著名的电影明星。

"她太可爱了，"黛西说。
"挨着她站着的那个男子是她的导演。"
他走了一圈，把我们介绍给所到之处的许多人：

"这是布坎南太太……这是布坎南先生——马球手。"

recognize ['rekəgnaiz] *vt.* 认出；承认；明白

bitterly ['bitəli] *ad.* 讽刺地，尖刻地；不满地，怨恨地

"I've never met so many famous people before," Daisy cried. "I liked that man we just met."

Gatsby told her the man's name and added that he was a famous filmmaker.

"Excuse me," said Tom to Gatsby, "but please don't introduce me as a polo player."

Tom walked off to talk with some women and Daisy and Gatsby danced. I was surprised to see his traditional way of dancing; he was quite good. After they finished we walked over to my house and Gatsby and Daisy sat on my stairs for half an hour, *while* I stood in the garden and watched to see where Tom was.

We then returned to the party and when we were sitting down to eat dinner, Tom appeared. "Do you mind if I eat with some people over there?" he asked Daisy.

"Of course not," Daisy answered, "and if you want to write down any of their addresses, here's my pen." She turned around after a minute and looked at Tom. She told me the girl sitting with Tom was "common but pretty". I understood then that, except for the half-hour she had been sitting alone with Gatsby, she wasn't *having* any *fun*.

The other people sitting at our table were all quite drunk. At the last party I had liked these same people, but now I was annoyed by their silly conversations. Daisy obviously did not enjoy the conversation either. I could see that she didn't like

"以前我从没见过这么多名人，"黛西叫道。"我喜欢刚才见过的那个人。"

盖茨比告诉她那人的名字，并补充说他是个著名的电影制片人。

"对不起，"汤姆对盖茨比说，"请别介绍我是马球手。"

汤姆走开和别的女人说话去了，黛西和盖茨比跳起了舞。我吃惊地看着他跳的是传统舞步；他跳得相当好。他们跳完舞，我们走到我家，盖茨比和黛西在台阶上坐了半个小时，我则站在花园里，注意看着汤姆在哪儿。

然后我们回到聚会上，当我们坐下来吃晚饭时，汤姆才露面。"你介意我和别人在那边吃饭吗？"他问黛西。

"当然不，"黛西回答道，"如果你想记下他们谁的地址我这儿有笔。"过了一会儿，她转过身去看汤姆。她告诉我，和汤姆坐在一块儿的那个女孩"平庸但很漂亮"。然后我意识到，除了她单独和盖茨比坐在一起的那半小时外，她一点儿也不开心。

和我们一桌的其他人都已喝得酩酊大醉。在上次聚会时我还挺喜欢这些人，但现在他们那愚蠢的谈话却让我厌烦了。黛西显然也不喜欢他们的谈话，我能看出她不喜欢西卵镇的社交场所。

while [wail] 时间从句，表示伴随的情况。

have fun 玩得高兴。如：We had fun riding our bicycles to the beach today. 今天我们骑车去海边玩得很开心。

133

West Egg *society*.

I sat on the stairs with Daisy and Tom while they waited for their car.

"Who is this Gatsby?" demanded Tom suddenly. "Is he some big *bootlegger*?"

"Who told you that?" I asked.

"Nobody, I just guessed it. Most of these newly rich people are bootleggers."

"Not Mr. Gatsby," I said, trying to hide the anger in my voice.

"Well, he must have worked hard to get this group of strange people together tonight."

"I'd like to know how he made all his money," insisted Tom. "And I plan to learn."

"I can tell you right now," Daisy said. "He owned a lot of medicine stores in Chicago. He made his money himself."

Their car finally came up the road.

"Goodnight, Nick," said Daisy.

I stayed very late that night. Gatsby asked me to wait for him until he was free, and I waited in his garden until the late night swimming party had ended. When he finally came to meet me his eyes were tired.

"She didn't like the party," he said immediately.

"Of course she did."

"She didn't," he insisted. "She didn't have a good

我坐在台阶上陪着黛西和汤姆等他们的车来。

"这个盖茨比是个什么人?"汤姆突然问。"他是个大私酒贩子吗?"

"谁告诉你的?"我问。

"没有人告诉我,我只是猜测。这些暴发户大多是大私酒贩子。"

"盖茨比先生不是,"我说话时尽力隐藏我生气的语气。

"那,他今晚一定是费了好大劲儿才把这群怪人凑到一块儿的。"

"我想知道他是怎样弄这么多钱的,"汤姆坚持说。"而且我打算跟他学。"

"我现在可以告诉你,"黛西说。"他在芝加哥拥有很多药店,他自己挣的钱。"

他们的车终于沿路开过来了。

"晚安,尼克,"黛西说。

那夜我待到很晚。盖茨比要我等到他闲下来,于是我就在他家花园里一直等到深夜游泳会结束。等到最后他来见我时,他的双眼已很疲卷了。

"她不喜欢这个聚会,"他立刻就说。

"她当然喜欢。"

"她不喜欢,"他坚持道。"她玩得不开心。"

society [sə'saiəty] *n.* 社交界,社交场所,社会生活方式

bootlegger [' buːtlegə] *n.* (酒等)非法制造(或运输、贩卖)的人。

135

time."

He stood there silently and I could feel the pain in his heart.

"I feel so *far away from* her," he said. "It's difficult to make her understand my feelings."

Gatsby then told me his dream. He wanted Daisy to say to Tom, "I never loved you." Then, after she left Tom, Gatsby and her *would go* back to Louisville *and be* married in her house — just as if it was five years ago.

"She doesn't understand," he said. "She used to understand. We would sit for hours talking."

"You shouldn't ask too much from her," I said. "You can't repeat the past."

"I can't repeat the past?" he cried shockedly. "Of course I can!"

He looked around wildly, as if the past was hidden in the trees and the shadow of his huge house, and was just a little too far for him to catch.

"I will fix everything just the same as it was in the past," he said firmly. "She will understand."

Gatsby often talked about his past, and I realized that he wanted to recover something, perhaps *some part of himself* that was alive *when* he and Daisy were in love. His life had been crazy since then; he believed that if he could return to the past and begin his life again slowly, he could learn what part of him

他静静地站在那儿，我能感觉到他心里很痛苦。

　　"我觉得离她很远，"他说。"很难让她明白我的感情。"

　　接着盖茨比告诉了我他的梦想。他想让黛西对汤姆说，"我从没爱过你。"然后，等她离开汤姆后，盖茨比就和她回到路易斯维尔，在她家和她结婚——就好像五年前一样。

　　"她不理解，"他说。"她原来挺善解人意的，那时我们俩常常坐在一块—谈就是几个小时。"

　　"你不应该对她要求太高，"我说。"你不能重温旧梦。"

　　"我不能重温旧梦?"他惊叫着，"当然能!"

　　他狂乱地扫视周围，好像过去就隐藏在树里，隐藏在他的大房子的阴影里，只差一点点就是够不着。

　　"我会把一切安排得就像过去一样，"他坚定地说。"她会明白的。"

　　盖茨比经常谈及他的过去，我意识到他是想把什么东西找回来，也许是和黛西恋爱时在他心里活着的某些东西。从那时起他的生活就癫狂了；他相信如果他能回到过去，重新慢慢地开始他的生活，他就能得知他失去的那部分是什么了。

far away from 远离…/离…很远

would go... and be... 这里and连接并列句，be前省略了would。

some part of himself 他自己的某部分（思想或经历）。

when [wen] *conj.* 作连词用，意为"一…就…""如果"

137

was now missing.

One autumn night, he said, five years ago, he and Daisy were walking down the street when the leaves were falling from the trees, and they came to a place where the street was empty and white with moonlight. They stopped there and moved close to each other.

As Daisy's white face came towards his own his heart jumped fast. He knew that when he kissed Daisy he would lose some of his own power. He would join his dreams to this human person forever. So he waited and listened to the music of the stars. Then he kissed her. At the moment when his lips touched hers, she became like a flower to him and the magic was born.

一个秋日的夜晚，他说，就在五年前，落叶潇潇的时候，他和黛西沿街走着，来到一个没人的地方，月光照得街道发白。他们停在那儿，互相靠近。

当黛西苍白的脸蛋贴过来时，他的心跳加快。他知道如果他亲吻黛西，他自己的力量就会失去一些。他会永远把自己的梦想都维系在这个女人身上。于是他等了等，聆听着繁星奏响的音乐。然后，他吻了她。就在他的嘴唇触到她的双唇的一刹那，她变成了为他而开的花朵，魔法出现了。

CHAPTER SEVEN An Afternoon Together

O ne Saturday night the lights in Gatsby's house did
not turn on. Many cars drove up his road, expecting
a party, but they all turned around after a minute and drove
sadly away.

I was worried that he was sick and went over to see him.

His door was opened by a new helper with an ugly face;
he gave me a strange look.

"Is Mr. Gatsby sick?" I asked.

"No." He said, then after a moment added "sir" in an
unhappy way.

I hadn't seen Gatsby for many days, and I was quite worried. "Please, tell him Mr. Carraway came over."

"Who?" he asked rudely.

"Mr. Carraway."

"Carraway. Fine, I'll tell him." He loudly shut the door.

I was later told that Gatsby had changed every servant in
his house a week before, and had *replaced* them *with* half a
dozen new ones. These new ones never went into West Egg village, but used the telephone to buy food and other things.
Many people in the village thought that the new people weren't
even servants.

Gatsby called me on the phone the very next day.

"Are you going away?" I asked.

第七章 共度下午

一个星期六的晚上盖茨比家的灯没有开亮。许多车都向他家路上开过来，希望有聚会，但一会儿他们都掉转车头，悻悻地开走了。

我担心他病了，就过去看他。

一个面相丑陋的新仆人开了门，他怪怪地看了我一眼。

"盖茨比先生病了吗?"我问。

"没有。"他说，停了一会儿才极不情愿地加上了"先生"两个字。

我好多天没见到盖茨比了，因此很担心他。"请告诉他，卡罗威先生过来了。"

"谁?"他粗鲁地问道。

"卡罗威先生。"

"卡罗威。好的，我告诉他。"他重重地关上门。

后来我被告知盖茨比一周前已更换了家里所有的仆人，来了六个新仆人。这些新仆人从来不去西卵村，而是打电话买食物和其他物品。村里许多人都认为这些人简直就不是仆人。

就在第二天，盖茨比打电话过来了。

"你出门了吗?"我问。

replace... with... 用…替换…

141

"No, young fellow."

"I hear you changed your servants."

" I wanted people who wouldn't talk." Gatsby said. "Daisy comes over often. These helpers are all people that Wolfshiem wanted to help. They used to run a small hotel together. They're all sisters and brothers."

"I see."

Gatsby called me because Daisy had asked him to. She wanted me to come over to her house for lunch tomorrow. Jordan would be there too. Later that day Daisy also telephoned me herself. She was worried on the phone, but she became calmer when I said that I would come. Something was *definitely* wrong.

It was extremely hot the next day, the hottest day of the whole summer. Gatsby drove me to the Buchanans' house.

Their living room was hidden from the sunlight; it was dark and cool. Daisy and Jordan were lying on the big sofa.

"It's too hot, we can't move," they said together.

Jordan's fingers rested for a moment in my hand.

Gatsby stood in the center of the room and *looked around*. Daisy watched him and laughed her warm, exciting laugh.

"Where is Mr. Thomas Buchanan, the polo player?" I joked. Then I heard his voice talking on the telephone.

"He is probably talking with his girlfriend," said Jordan.

We all listened silently. Tom's voice became high with

"没有，老兄。"

"我听说你换了仆人。"

"我想要些不会多嘴的人。"盖茨比说。"黛西经常过来。这些仆人都是沃尔夫山姆想帮一把的人。他们过去一起经营了一家小旅馆，他们都是兄弟姐妹。"

"我明白了。"

盖茨比给我打电话是因为黛西要他打的。她想叫我第二天去她家吃午饭。乔丹也去。当天晚些时候她又亲自打电话给我。电话里她很担心，但当我答应去后，她平静了许多。肯定是出什么事了。

第二天天气相当热，是整个夏季最热的一天。盖茨比开车带我去了布坎南家。

他家的客厅在树荫下；又暗又凉块。黛西和乔丹躺在大沙发上。

"太热了，我们都没法动了。"她们齐声说。

乔丹的手指在我手上放了一会儿。

盖茨比站在屋子中间，四下里望着。黛西望着他，热情、兴奋地笑着。

"汤姆·布坎南先生，那个马球手去哪儿啦？"我开玩笑地说。这时我听到他正在打电话。

"他可能正在给女朋友打电话，"乔丹说。

我们都静静地听着。汤姆的声音因愤怒

definitely ['definitli] *ad.* 明确地、清楚地，一定地、肯定地

look around 环顾，往四下看

143

anger, "Okay, fine, I won't sell you the car then ... and don't ask me about it at lunch time!"

Tom loudly threw open the door and came into the room.

"Mr. Gatsby!" He shook Gatsby's hand, hiding his hate for him. "I'm happy to see you, sir ... happy to see you too, Nick ... "

"Make us cold drinks," cried Daisy.

When Tom left the room, Daisy stood up and went over to Gatsby and kissed him on the mouth.

"I love you," she whispered.

At that moment the nurse came into the room. She was leading a little girl in a pretty white dress.

"My loved one!" cried Daisy. "Come here to your mother!"

The child *hurried across* the room to Daisy and hid her face in her mother's skirt.

"Lovely child! Come shake hands."

Gatsby and I both *sat down on one knee* and shook the small girl's hand. Gatsby looked at the child with surprise. I didn't think he had really believed in her existence before.

"She doesn't look like Tom," said Daisy. "She looks just like me. She has my hair and eyes." Daisy bent her face down to the child. "You're my little dream!"

Then she again sat back on the sofa.

"Goodbye, love!" she then said. "Go back to your

而变大："那么，好吧，到时我不会把汽车卖给你……午饭时别问我这事！"

汤姆猛地推开门，走进屋里，声音很大。

"盖茨比先生！"他握着盖茨比的手，心里隐藏着对他的恨。"很高兴见到你，先生……尼克，也很高兴见到你……"

"弄点冷饮来吧，"黛西大声叫道。

汤姆离开屋子时，黛西站起来，走到盖茨比跟前，亲了一下他的嘴。

"我爱你，"她悄声说。

这时保姆领着一个穿着漂亮白裙子的小女孩走进来。

"宝贝！"黛西大声说道。"来妈妈这儿！"

那小孩匆匆走过屋子，来到黛西跟前，把脸藏在妈妈的裙子里。

"可爱的宝贝，过来握握手。"

盖茨比和我都半单膝跪地握了握那小姑娘的手。盖茨比吃惊地看着小姑娘。我想他以前从未真正相信过她的存在。

"她长得不像汤姆，"黛西说。"看上去就像我，长着和我一样的头发和眼睛。"黛西俯着脸对着孩子说，"你是我的小乖乖！"

然后她又坐回到沙发上。

"再见，亲爱的！"她接着说，"回你屋吧。"

hurry across 赶紧、匆忙穿过…

sit down on one knee 单腿跪着。"双膝跪着"则是sit down on one's knees。

room."

The nurse grasped the child's hand and pulled her out of the room, the child looked like she missed her mother.

Tom came back with the cold drinks.

"Come with me outside," Tom suggested to Gatsby, "I want you to see our place."

I joined them outside. The ocean was dark green and silent in the hot weather. Gatsby pointed across the water.

"My house is right across from you."

We had lunch in the dining room; it was also hidden from the heat. Everyone talked nervously.

"What should we do this afternoon?" cried Daisy, "and tomorrow, and for the next thirty years?"

"Don't worry," said Jordan. "Life will start again when the weather turns cool in the fall."

"But it's so hot," said Daisy, almost crying, "and life is so boring. Let's all go to the city!"

Tom and Gatsby were talking about horses.

"Who wants to go to the city?" demanded Daisy. Gatsby looked towards her. She looked back and cried, "You look so *cool*!"

Their eyes stared at each other, alone in the universe. Then Daisy quickly looked down at the floor.

"You always look so cool," she said again. It was her way of saying that she loved him, and Tom Buchanan under-

保姆抓住孩子的手把她拉出屋子，孩子看上去很留恋她的妈妈。

汤姆带着冷饮回来了。

"跟我到外面去，"汤姆向盖茨比建议，"我想让你看看我们这地方。"

我也跟着他们出去了。大海是深绿色的，在酷热中平静无浪。盖茨比用手指着海水对面。

"我的房子正对着你们。"

我们在餐厅里吃午饭；那儿也避开了热浪。每人说话时都有点紧张。

"我们今天下午该干什么？"黛西大声说道，"明天呢，以后三十年呢？"

"别担心，"乔丹说。"秋天天气变凉快了，生活就又会重新开始了。"

"但是天这么热，生活又这么没意思，我们都到城里去吧！"黛西说话时几乎要哭出来。

汤姆和盖茨比在谈论着有关马的事。

"谁想去城里？"黛西问。盖茨比看着她，她也看着盖茨比，大声说道，"你看着真潇洒！"

他们的眼睛对视着，世界上只剩他们俩。然后黛西赶紧低头看着地板。

"你看上去总是那么潇洒。"她又说了一遍。这是她说爱他的一种方式，汤姆·布坎南

cool [ku:l] *adj.* 给人凉快感觉的；形容人冷静的、沉着的、从容的。

147

stood. He was shocked. His mouth opened a little bit, and he stared at Gatsby, and then at Daisy.

"You look like the actor in that famous movie," she then said. "You know, the movie where — "

"All right," Tom quickly interrupted, "I'm willing to go to the city. Yes, we're all going to the city."

Tom stood up, his eyes still staring at Gatsby and his wife. No one else moved.

" Let's go! " The anger in his voice was increasing. "What's the problem? If you want to go to the city, let's go now."

"Are we just going to go now?" Daisy asked, "Shouldn't we let everyone smoke a cigarette first?"

"Everybody smoked during lunch."

"Fine," she said. "Come on, Jordan."

They went upstairs to change clothes.

"Should we take anything to drink?" yelled Daisy from upstairs.

" I'll get some wine," answered Tom. He went to the kitchen.

Gatsby *turned to* me.

"I can't say anything in his house, young fellow."

" Daisy's voice tells Tom her feelings for you," I said. "Her voice is full of — " I paused.

"Her voice is full of money," Gatsby said suddenly.

明白。他惊讶地微微张了一下嘴，盯着盖茨比，然后又盯着黛西。

"你像那个著名电影里的演员，"黛西接着说。"你知道，那个电影——"

汤姆急忙打断了她，"好吧，我愿意去城里，是的，我们都去城里。"

汤姆站起来，眼睛仍然盯着盖茨比和他的妻子。其他人都坐着没动。

"走吧!"他声音里火气大了起来。"到底怎么回事?如果你们想去城里，那现在就走哇。"

"现在我们就这么去吗?"黛西问，"我们不该让大家先抽根烟吗?"

"午饭时大家都抽过烟了。"

"好的，"她说。"乔丹，过来。"
她们上楼去换衣服。

"我们带点儿喝的吗?"黛西从楼上喊道。

"我拿点酒，"汤姆回答道。他走到厨房。

盖茨比向我求助。

"在他家，我什么也说不出来，老兄。"
"黛西的声音告诉了汤姆她对你的感情，"我说。"她的声音充满了——"我止住了。
"她的声音里充满了金钱。"盖茨比突然说。

turn to 求助于；求教于。例如：You can always turn to me for help. 你随时可以找我来帮忙。

149

Yes! He was right! She had the voice of a rich girl, a princess — that was its magic power.

Tom came back holding a bottle in a towel, followed by Daisy and Jordan.

"Shall we all go together in my car?" suggested Gatsby.

"No, you drive mine," said Tom, "and let me drive yours."

Gatsby did not like this idea.

"I don't think there's much gas in my car," he said.

"I will stop at the store," said Tom. He looked at Gatsby with a strange look in his eyes.

A very strange smile appeared on Gatsby's face. "Okay, you take my car."

"Let's go, Daisy," said Tom. He pulled her towards Gatsby's car, but she *moved away from* him.

"You take Nick and Jordan," she said. "I'll go in your car."

She walked close to Gatsby. Jordan, Tom and I got into Gatsby's car, and drove off.

"Did you see that?" demanded Tom.

"See what?"

He stared at me angrily. He realized that Jordan and I had known about Daisy and Gatsby for a long time. Tom was not a good man, but he was not a stupid man either.

"I've learned many things about this Gatsby," said Tom.

是的!他说得对!她有着一个富家女孩、一个公主的声音——那就是它的魔力。

汤姆用一条毛巾包着一瓶酒走回来,后面跟着黛西和乔丹。

"我们一块儿坐我的车好吗?"盖茨比建议道。

"不,你们开我的车,"汤姆说,"我来开你的车。"

盖茨比不喜欢这个主意。

"我想我的车里没多少汽油了,"他说。

"我就停在商店门口,"汤姆说。他看着盖茨比,眼睛里有种异样的光。

盖茨比的脸上露出很奇怪的笑容。"好吧,你开我的车。"

"走吧,黛西,"汤姆说。他把她拉向盖茨比的车,但她从他手里挣脱了。

"你带上尼克和乔丹,"她说,"我坐你的车。"

她走近盖茨比。乔丹、汤姆和我钻进盖茨比的车里开走了。

"你看见了吗?"汤姆问。

"看见什么?"

他生气地盯着我。他意识到乔丹和我早就知道黛西和盖茨比的事了。汤姆不是好人,但也不是傻瓜。

"我已经知道这个盖茨比的许多事情,"

move away from 从…移开

151

"I've asked some people about his history."

"And you learned that he was an Oxford student," said Jordan.

"An Oxford student! It's not possible!"

"Why did you invite him for lunch, then, if you don't like him?" demanded Jordan.

"I didn't! Daisy invited him; she said that she knew him before we were married — who knows where!"

For a while we drove in angry silence. Then when I saw the dirty sign with Doctor T.J. Eckleburg's eyes on it, I remembered that Gatsby said the car didn't have much gasoline.

"We have enough gasoline to get us to the city," said Tom.

"But there's a garage right here," said Jordan.

Tom stopped the car at Wilson's sign. Wilson came outside and stared at the car unhappily.

"Hurry!" yelled Tom roughly. "Why do you think we stopped — to watch the view?"

"I've been sick all day," said Wilson, not moving.

"Shall I get my own gasoline?" Tom demanded. "You didn't *sound* sick on the phone."

Wilson walked slowly toward the car and began to fill it with gasoline. His face looked green in the sun.

"I'm sorry that I called you on the phone and interrupted your lunch before," Wilson said. "But I need some money

汤姆说。"关于他的历史我已问过一些人。"

"而且你了解到他是牛津大学的学生，"乔丹说。

"牛津大学学生!不可能!"

"既然你不喜欢他，那你为什么还邀请他吃午饭呢?"乔丹问。

"我没有!是黛西邀请的;她说我们结婚前她就认识他——谁知道是在哪儿!"

在愤怒和沉默的气氛中我们开车走了一段时间。然后当我看见上面有T·J·爱克尔堡医生的眼睛的那块脏兮兮的标牌，我想起盖茨比说汽车没有多少汽油了。

"汽油足够我们开到市里，"汤姆说。

"但这儿正好有一家车行，"乔丹说。

汤姆在威尔逊的牌子旁停下了车。威尔逊走出来，郁郁不乐地盯着这辆汽车。

"快点!"汤姆粗鲁地嚷道。"你认为我们停下来是——看风景的吗?"

"我病了一整天，"威尔逊说，人一动没动。

"我得自己加油吗?"汤姆问。"电话里没听出来你病了。"

威尔逊慢慢地走向汽车，开始加油，在太阳底下他的脸成了绿色。

"我很抱歉前些时候打电话打扰你吃午饭，"威尔逊说。"可我急需一些钱，我想知

sound [saund] *vi.* 听起来;似乎

153

quickly, and I wanted to know when you were going to sell your old car."

"Do you like this one?" asked Tom. "I just bought it."

"It's a fancy car," said Wilson. "But I could really make some money on your other one."

"Why do you want money so quickly; before you said your money was okay?"

"I've been living here too long. My wife and I want to leave New York and go to the West."

"Your wife wants to leave?" cried Tom.

"She's wanted to leave for ten years. And now she's moving if she wants to or not. I've just learned that something very strange is happening. I'm going to take her far away. That's why I need money now."

"How much for the gas?" demanded Tom roughly.

"Two dollars."

I realized that Wilson still didn't realize that Tom was sleeping with his wife secretly. Wilson had discovered that his wife had a secret life away in a different world, and the shock had made him become ill.

"I'll sell you my old car," said Tom. "Tomorrow."

I then realized that in one of the windows over the garage Mrs. Wilson was staring down at the car. Her eyes were full of jealous anger. She was staring at Jordan Baker, whom she must have thought was Tom's wife.

道您打算什么时候卖您那辆旧车。"

"你喜欢这辆吗?"汤姆问。 "我刚买的。"

"是辆迷人的车,"威尔逊说。"但我真的能在您的另一辆车上挣点钱。"

"你为什么如此急着用钱,从前你说你的钱够用。"

"我住这儿太久了。我妻子和我想离开纽约到西部去。"

"你妻子想离开?"汤姆大声问道。

"她想走已经十年了,现在不管她想走不想走她都得走。我刚知道出了点儿怪事。我要把她带得远远的。所以我现在需要钱。"

"汽油多少钱?"汤姆粗鲁地问。
"两美元。"

我意识到威尔逊仍然不知道汤姆一直秘密地和他妻子同居。威尔逊已经发现他妻子在另一个世界过着一种秘密的生活,一番惊吓就把他弄病了。

"我会把我的旧车卖给你,"汤姆说。"明天。"

紧接着我突然意识到在车行上面的一扇窗户里,威尔逊太太正往下盯着这辆车。她的眼睛里充满了妒忌、恼怒。她正盯着乔丹·贝克,她一定以为这就是汤姆的妻子。

Tom drove quickly towards New York. The fear and doubt in his simple mind were clear. An hour before he had a wife and a girlfriend — and now they were both disappearing.

We caught up with Gatsby and Daisy and *argued about* how to spend the afternoon. Jordan wanted to see a movie; Daisy suggested that we rent a hotel room and take cold baths. Finally, for no real reason, we decided to rent a sitting room in a hotel and drink some wine.

The air inside the large room did not move, we opened the windows, but it only let in some hot air.

"Open more windows!" Daisy said.

"There aren't any more windows." Tom said.

"Well, then telephone the manager and ask for a hammer — "

"Don't think about the heat," said Tom sharply. "Talking about it only makes it feel worse."

"Let her talk, young fellow." said Gatsby.

There was a moment of silence.

"You always say 'young fellow'. Where'd you learn to say that?"

"*Be polite*, Tom," said Daisy, "if you are going to be rude I'll leave. Call up and order some ice for the drinks."

Tom picked up the telephone and ordered some ice and drinks. Then he started talking to me about our college days. Suddenly, he turned towards Gatsby.

汤姆快速开向纽约。显然他那简单的头脑里充满了害怕和怀疑。一小时前他既有妻子又有女朋友——可现在她们俩都要消失了。

我们追上盖茨比和黛西，争论怎么打发这个下午。乔丹想去看电影；黛西建议我们在旅馆租个房，洗个冷水澡。最后，也没什么真正的理由，我们决定在旅馆租一个客厅，然后喝点酒。

宽大的房子里空气却不流通，我们打开窗子，但进来的只有热风。

"再多开几扇窗户！"黛西说。
"再没有窗户啦。"汤姆说。

"那，打电话跟经理要个锤子——"

"别老想着天热，"汤姆严厉地说。"谈论天热只会使人感觉天更热。"

"让她说吧，老兄。"盖茨比说。
沉默了一会儿。

"你总是说'老兄'。你在哪儿学的？"

"礼貌点，汤姆，"黛西说，"如果你打算无礼，那我就走。打电话要点冰块放到饮料里。"

汤姆拿起电话，定了一些冰块和饮料。然后他开始跟我谈我们大学里的生活。突然他转向盖茨比。

argue about = argue on (over) 辩论（争论）某事。

be polite 礼貌点。如：Be polite and do right thing. 举止文雅，循规蹈矩。

"Mr. Gatsby, I hear you went to Oxford."

"Not really."

"Oh, yes, I heard you studied there."

"Yes — I went there."

There was a pause. Then Tom's voice, scolding and not believing, "I wonder when you could have been there?"

Again, there was a pause. A waiter entered with ice, and closed the door softly. We all looked at Gatsby. This important part of his history was finally going to be told.

"I told you I went there," Gatsby said.

"Yes, I heard you. I'd like to know when."

"In 1919, I only studied there for five months. I can't really say that I am an Oxford student. It was an opportunity that the army gave to some of the officers after the war."

I was very happy to hear Gatsby's words. My *belief in him* returned.

Daisy smiled. "Open the wine, Tom, and I'll make you a drink."

"Wait!" yelled Tom. "I want to ask Mr. Gatsby another question."

"Please ask," Gatsby said politely.

"What kind of trouble are you making in my house?"

The secret was now in the open. Tom was ready to fight.

"He isn't making trouble," said Daisy. "You're making trouble, Tom. Please calm yourself."

"盖茨比先生，我听说你上过牛津大学。"

"不确切。"

"噢，是的，我听说你在那儿读过书。"

"是的——我去过那儿。"

一阵停顿。然后汤姆带着质疑和不信任的口气问道："我想知道你什么时候可能去那儿的？"

又一阵停顿。侍者端着冰块走进来，并轻轻关上门。我们都看着盖茨比。他过去这一重要部分就要被最后揭开了。

"我告诉你我去过那儿，"盖茨比说。

"是的，我听你说过。我想知道是什么时候。"

"在1919年，我在那儿只读了五个月。我不能说自己是一个真正的牛津学生。这是战后军队给部分军官的一个机会。"

听到盖茨比的这些话我很高兴。我对他的信任又回来了。

黛西笑了。"打开酒，汤姆，我要让你喝一杯。"

"等等！"汤姆叫道。"我要问盖茨比先生另一个问题。"

"请问吧，"盖茨比礼貌地说。

"你想在我家制造什么样的麻烦？"

秘密终于公开了。汤姆准备打架了。

"他没有惹麻烦，"黛西说。"你在惹麻烦，汤姆。请冷静点儿。"

belief in sb. 对某人的信任。
belief 是believe的名词形式。

159

"Calm myself! Do you expect me to stand here and do nothing while Mr. Nobody from nowhere sleeps with my wife?"

"I want to tell you something," said Gatsby. "Your wife never loved you. She loves me."

"You're crazy!" cried Tom.

Gatsby jumped up from his chair. "She only married you because I was poor and she was tired of waiting for me to come back from the war. It was a terrible mistake, but in her heart she only loved me!"

"Daisy!" cried Tom. "How long have you been seeing this man?"

"I already told you," said Gatsby. "We've been in love for five years."

Tom turned sharply to Daisy.

"You've been seeing this young fellow for five years?"

"No," said Gatsby. "No, we were not able to see each other. But we were in love all that time."

"That's a lie!" Tom yelled. "Daisy loved me when we were married and she still loves me now. I love Daisy too. Sometimes I go out on a little adventure with another woman, but I always come back, and in my heart I always love her."

"You're terrible," shouted Daisy. She turned towards me. "Do you know why we had to leave Chicago? Have you heard the story of that 'little adventure'?"

"Daisy, that is in the past now," said Gatsby. "Just tell

"让我冷静!你们都希望我站在这儿不管不问,任凭不知从哪儿来的无名先生跟我老婆睡觉吗?"

"我想告诉你一点事,"盖茨比说。"你妻子从来都没爱过你。她爱的是我。"

"你疯了!"汤姆叫道。

盖茨比从椅子上跳起来。"她嫁给你只是因为我很穷,而她又等不及我从战场上归来。这是一个可怕的错误,但在她心里她只爱我!"

"黛西!"汤姆叫道。"你一直和这个人见面有多长时间了?"

"我已经告诉过你,"盖茨比说。"我们已经相爱五年了。"

汤姆径直转向黛西。

"你一直和这家伙见面已经五年啦?"

"不,"盖茨比说。"不,我们彼此不能见面,但我们一直相爱着。"

"那是撒谎!"汤姆大叫道。"我们结婚时,黛西爱我,现在她依然爱我。我也爱黛西。有时偶尔出去和别的女人来点儿小小的冒险,可我总是回来,并且在我心里我一直爱着她。"

"你真恶心,"黛西喊道。她转向我。"你知道我们为什么得离开芝加哥吗?你听说过那些'小小冒险'的故事吗?"

"黛西,现在那些都已经过去了。"盖茨

him the truth — that you have never loved him."

Daisy looked at Gatsby, but her eyes were empty.

"Say that you never loved him!" repeated Gatsby.

She paused. "I never loved him," she said with a nervous voice.

"Not on our wedding?" demanded Tom.

"No."

"Not on that day when it rained and I carried you home to keep your shoes dry?" There was softness and love in Tom's voice.

"Please don't speak!" Daisy cried. She tried to light a cigarette, but her hands were shaking. Suddenly, she threw the cigarette down on the floor.

"You want too much!" she cried to Gatsby. "I love you now and have loved you for five years — isn't that enough? I can't change what is in the past. Yes, I did love Tom once — but I loved you too."

"Even that is a lie," said Tom. "During these years she never thought about you."

Tom's words seemed to go into Gatsby's heart like a knife.

"I want to speak to Daisy alone," Gatsby said.

"Even alone I can't say I never loved Tom." Daisy's voice was shaking. "It wouldn't be true."

"Of course it wouldn't," said Tom. "Don't worry, Daisy, from now on I'm going to take care of you."

比说。"就告诉他真相——你从来都没爱过他。"

黛西看着盖茨比，但她的眼睛里一片茫然。

"说你从未爱过他！"盖茨比重复道。

她停了一会，然后用紧张的语气说："我从没爱过他。"

"我们结婚时你也不爱我吗？"汤姆问。

"不爱。"

"那天下雨我怕弄湿了你的鞋子背你回家时你也不爱我吗？"汤姆的声音里有种温柔和爱意。

"求你别说啦！"黛西哭喊道。她想点一支烟，但她的手抖得厉害。她突然把烟扔到了地板上。

"你要得太多了！"她冲着盖茨比叫道。"我现在爱你，并且爱了你五年——这还不够吗？我不能改变过去的一切。是的，我曾经确实爱过汤姆——但我也爱你。"

"连这也是撒谎，"汤姆说。"这些年她从未想过你。"

汤姆的话像一把刀一样刺进了盖茨比的心脏。

"我想单独和黛西谈谈，"盖茨比说。

"就是单独谈，我也不能说我从没爱过汤姆。"黛西的声音颤抖着。"这不可能是真的。"

"当然不可能，"汤姆说。"不用担心，黛西，从现在起我会好好照顾你的。"

"You don't understand," said Gatsby. "You're not going to take care of her any more."

"I'm not?" Tom laughed. "Why's that?"

"Daisy *is leaving* you."

"You're truly crazy." Tom yelled.

"Yes, I am leaving you, Tom," Daisy said nervously.

"No, she's not leaving me! She definitely won't replace me with a dishonest young fellow like you! Who are you, Mr. Gatsby? You work with Meyer Wolfshiem — I've learned about your affairs!"

"I won't listen to this!" cried Daisy. "Let's leave!"

"I know what your 'medicine stores' were. You and this Wolfshiem bought a lot of medicine stores here and in Chicago and used them to sell *illegal alcohol*. My friend David told me. But now you and Wolfshiem are doing something even more terrible — it is so terrible that David is afraid to talk about it."

I looked at Gatsby; he had a terrible expression on his face. Then his expression changed, and he began talking to Daisy in a nervous and excited voice. But she was not listening to him, so he stopped talking. Her courage was definitely gone. She asked again to leave.

"You two go home," said Tom. "Go in Mr. Gatsby's car. He won't trouble you now — he realizes that your time together is over."

They left silently. After a moment Tom stood up and be-

"你不明白，"盖茨比说。"你再也不能照顾她啦。"

"我不能?"汤姆大笑。"那是为什么?"

"黛西要离开你了。"

"你真是疯了。"汤姆大叫道。

"是的，汤姆，我要离开你，"黛西不安地说。

"不，她不会离开我!她绝对不愿意用你这样一个不诚实的家伙来代替我!你是谁，盖茨比先生?你和迈耶·沃尔夫山姆一块干——我了解你们的勾当!"

"我不想听这个!"黛西大声说。"我们离开吧!"

"我知道你的'药店'是什么。你和这个沃尔夫山姆在这儿和芝加哥买了很多药店，用它们非法出售酒。我朋友戴维告诉我的。但现在你和沃尔夫山姆正在干更可怕的事——太可怕了，以至戴维都不敢谈及此事。"

我看着盖茨比;他脸上有一种可怕的表情。然后他的表情变了，他开始用紧张而兴奋的语调跟黛西说话。但她不听他的，因此他停住不说了。她的勇气肯定消失了，她再次要离开。

"你们俩回家，"汤姆说。"坐盖茨比先生的车。他现在不会烦你了——他知道你们在一起的时间已经结束了。"

他们静静地离开了。过了一会儿，汤姆

be leaving 用 arrive, come, go, leave等动词的现在进行时描写行程安排，通常有"将到达"和"将离去"的意思。例如：1. He's arriving tomorrow morning on the 13:27 train. 明天早上他将乘13时27分的火车到达。2. I'm leaving England. 我即将离开英国。

illegal alcohol 指非法出售酒。

gan putting the bottle of wine back in the towel.

"Do you want this wine, Nick?"

I didn't answer.

"Nick?"

"What?"

"Do you want any wine?"

"No ... I just remembered that today is my thirtieth birthday."

It was already six o'clock when Tom, Jordan and I got into the car and drove back to East Egg.

I was sad to be thirty years old. Most of my friends were married, but I was still alone. I was getting older and my hair was disappearing. However, Jordan was beside me and she was smarter than Daisy. Still, I knew inside that I did not love her.

So we continued driving, towards the future and towards death.

站起来，开始把那瓶酒又用毛巾包起来。

"你想来点儿酒吗，尼克？"

我没有回答。

"尼克？"

"什么？"

"你要来点儿酒吗？"

"不要……我刚想起来今天是我三十岁生日。"

汤姆，乔丹和我进车往西卵镇返时，已是六点钟了。

三十岁了，我有点伤感。我的朋友大部分已经结婚了，但我仍孤身一人。我正在变老，头发渐稀。好歹有乔丹在我身边，她比黛西明智多了。不过我心里仍清楚我不爱她。

就这样我们向着未来和死亡继续前行。

CHAPTER EIGHT The Yellow Car

O nly one person saw the car accident clearly. It was the owner of the cafe next to the garage; his name was Michaelis. He told the story to the police when they came.

Michaelis had walked over to the garage a little bit after five and he found George Wilson there sitting in his office. Mr. Wilson was really sick, and his face was pale white. Michaelis *suggested* that he go rest, but Wilson refused. Then Michaelis heard a terrible noise upstairs.

"I've locked my wife in the bedroom," explained Wilson. "I'm going to keep her there for two days, and then we're going to move west."

Michaelis was quite shocked; he had been the Wilsons' neighbor for five years. He knew that Wilson was not the kind of man who would lock his wife in a room. So Michaelis asked Wilson what had happened, but Wilson wouldn't talk, so Michaelis went back to his cafe.

At about seven o'clock Michaelis heard Mrs. Wilson's voice yelling loudly in the garage. A minute later she ran out into the road, shouting and shaking her hand in the air.

Two cars were coming down the road, one was moving east and the other was moving west. One of the cars didn't stop and it hit Myrtle Wilson. The car then kept moving and disappeared around the next corner. The other car, the one going

第八章 黄色轿车

只有一个人清楚地目睹了车祸，是车行隔壁咖啡馆的老板，名叫米歇里斯。等警察来后，他描述了事情的经过。

五点过后一点儿，米歇里斯去车行，发现乔治·威尔逊坐在办公室里。威尔逊先生真的病了，脸色苍白。米歇里斯建议他去休息，但威尔逊不听。接着米歇里斯听到楼上传来可怕的吵闹声。

"我把妻子锁在卧室里了，"威尔逊解释道。"我打算把她关两天，然后我们打算搬到西部去。"

米歇里斯非常吃惊；他做威尔逊的邻居已经五年了。他知道威尔逊不是那种会把妻子锁在屋里的人。因此米歇里斯就问威尔逊出了什么事，但威尔逊没吭声，于是米歇里斯就回咖啡馆了。

大约七点钟时米歇里斯听到威尔逊太太在车行里大声尖叫。过了一会儿她跑出来，在路上叫着，挥着手。

两辆汽车开过来，一个往东开，一个往西开。其中一辆没有停下来，正好撞到茉特尔·威尔逊。那辆汽车继续往前冲，然后在下一个拐角附近消失了。往西的那辆车停了下

suggest [səˈdʒest] 这里的及物动词suggest表示"建议"，其后面宾语从句中的谓语动词多由should+动词原形构成，should可以省略，如本句。再如：I suggested (that) they drive along the coast. 我建议他们沿着海岸开车。

169

west, stopped, and the driver ran over to where Mrs. Wilson lay in the road, her blood was mixing with the dirt in the road. She was already dead.

When we drove by later we saw a crowd of people outside of the garage. "It must be an accident!" said Tom. "Let's go and look." He stopped his car, and we all jumped out. We could hear the sound of crying coming from inside and we saw that all of the people inside had serious faces.

"There has been some terrible trouble here," said Tom excitedly.

He pushed violently through the crowd and Jordan and I followed him.

Mrs. Wilson's body was lying on a table. A policeman stood next to it; he was writing down names in a black book. Wilson was standing in the door of his office and crying.

Tom asked the policeman, "What happened?"

"A car hit her. She was killed *instantly*. She ran out into the road and the driver didn't even stop his car."

"It was a big, yellow car," said Michaelis.

Mr. Wilson heard this. "I know what kind of car it was, you don't have to tell me!"

When Tom heard this he walked over to Mr. Wilson and said, "Listen to me. I just arrived here from New York. I was bringing my car here to sell you. That yellow car I was driving before wasn't mine — do you understand?" He then picked

来，司机跑到威尔逊太太躺在路上的地方，血混合着路上的灰尘。她已经死了。

当我们后来开车路过车行时，看见车行外面有一大群人。"一定是出什么事啦!"汤姆说。"我们过去看看。"他停下车，我们都跳出车来。我们能听到里面传出哭喊的声音，看到里面所有的人表情都很严肃。

"这儿出大乱子了，"汤姆兴奋地说。

他粗暴地挤过人群，乔丹和我跟在他后面。

威尔逊太太的尸体放在桌子上。一个警察站在旁边；他正在往黑色本子里记名字。威尔逊站在办公室的门里面，哭着。

汤姆问警察，"怎么啦?"

"车撞了她。她立刻就死了。她跑出去到了路当中，司机连车都没停。"

"是一辆黄色大轿车，"米歇里斯说。

威尔逊先生听到这话了："我知道那是怎样一辆车，你不用告诉我!"

汤姆听到这，便走到威尔逊先生身边说，"听我说。我刚从纽约到这儿，我把车开来卖给你。先前我开的那辆黄车不是我的——你明白吗?"然后他把威尔逊拽了起来，把他拉进

instantly ['instəntli] *adv.* =
at once 立刻，即刻

171

up Wilson, and pulled him into the office and put him down in a chair.

"We should leave," Tom whispered to me. We pushed our way outside and out to the car.

As Tom sped towards East Egg I saw that he was crying.

"*That* Gatsby is a coward!" he cried. "He didn't even stop his car after he hit her."

We quickly arrived at the Buchanans' house.

"Daisy's at home," said Tom, looking up at three windows with light in them. He then turned to me. "Sorry, I should have driven you to West Egg. I'll call a taxi for you."

Jordan grasped my hand and asked me if I would come inside with her, but I refused. I was feeling ill and I wanted to be alone. I *was sick of* looking at these people, and now that included Jordan also. She could see my feelings in my face, so she turned around sharply and ran into the house. I began walking down the road.

A moment later I heard somebody say my name, and I saw Gatsby hiding behind a tree.

"What are you doing?" I asked.

"I'm just standing here, young fellow." He looked up at the sky and then asked, "On the way home did you see any problems on the road?"

"Yes." I said.

He paused for a moment. "Was she killed?"

办公室，按到椅子上。

"我们应该离开，"汤姆低声对我说。我们挤出屋子，回到外面车上。

当汤姆把车开向东卵镇时我看见他在哭。

"那个盖茨比是个懦夫！"他叫道。"撞了她后连车都不停。"

我们很快到了布坎南的家。

"黛西在家，"汤姆抬头看着亮着灯的三个窗户说。然后他转向我。"对不起，我本该开车送你回西卵镇，我打电话给你叫辆出租车。"

乔丹抓住我的手，问我能否跟她一块儿进去，但我拒绝了。我感觉不舒服，我想一个人呆会儿。我讨厌看到这些人，现在也包括乔丹。她能看出我脸上的表情，于是她猛地扭转身，跑进屋子里去了。我开始沿路走着。

过了一会儿，我听见有人喊我的名字，我看见盖茨比躲在一棵树后面。

"你在干什么?"我问。

"我刚站到这儿，老兄。"他抬头望着天空，然后问，"在回来的路上你们看到什么事了吗?"

"看到了。"我说。

他停了一会说。"她死了吗?"

that [ðæt] *conj.* 这里表达一种厌烦、不满的感情色彩。

be sick of 厌烦、讨厌。后面接名词、代词或动名词。例如：1. John is sick of his job. 约翰不喜欢他的工作。2. I am sick of them.我讨厌他们。3. It was hot in the afternoon and I was sick of lying in bed.下午天气很热，我不喜欢总是躺在床上。

"Yes." I nodded my head.

"I thought we killed her; I told Daisy that she was probably dead. The best thing is to hear all of the shock at once. Daisy was very brave about it." Gatsby spoke as if the *effect* of the accident on Daisy was more important than the death of a person.

"I went back to West Egg quickly," he went on, "and I left my car in the garage. I don't think anybody saw the accident."

I was so angry at him that I didn't tell him that he had been seen.

"Who was the woman?" he asked.

"She and her husband own the garage. Her name was Myrtle Wilson. How did it happen?"

Gatsby thought for a moment and then began to speak. "Well, I tried to turn the wheel but — " He then paused, and suddenly I guessed the truth.

"You weren't driving!" I said. "Was Daisy driving?"

"Yes, she was," he said after a moment. "But I'll tell everyone that I was driving of course. When we left New York she was very nervous and upset, and she thought that a drive would help her become calm. Daisy was driving fast and this woman jumped out into the street just as a car was coming the other way. It seemed like the woman wanted to speak to us. Maybe she thought that she knew us. Daisy turned the wheel

"死了。"我点点头。

"我想是我们杀了她；我告诉黛西她可能会死。最好的事情就是立刻听到所有的震动，黛西对此事一点也不怕。"盖茨比的意思好像是说这个事故对黛西的影响比死一个人更重要。

"我很快回到西卵镇，"他继续说，"我把车停在车库里。我想没有人看见这场事故。"

我对他非常生气，因此没有告诉他有人已看见他了。

"那个女人是谁?"他问。

"她和她丈夫是那车行的老板，她的名字叫茉特尔·威尔逊。这是怎么回事儿?"

盖茨比想了一会儿，开始说话了。"哦，我尽力扭转方向盘，但是——"他然后停住了，我突然间猜出了真相。

"你没开车!"我说。"是黛西开车吧?"

"是的，是她开车。"他过了一会儿说。"但是我当然要告诉大家是我在开车。当我们离开纽约时她非常紧张，情绪低落，她认为开车能帮她平静下来。黛西开得很快，正当一辆车从对面开过来时，这个女人从屋里飞跑到路上，好像要跟我们说话。也许她以为认识我们。黛西打方向盘，躲开了这女人，但接着怕撞着另一辆车，于是又迅速把方向盘打了回

effect [i'fekt] *n.*影响、作用。这里用作名词，表示"对…的影响"，后面要接on。

175

away from the woman, but then she was afraid of hitting the other car, so she quickly turned the wheel back. I felt us hit the woman and I tried to make Daisy stop, but she wouldn't.

"She'll be fine tomorrow," he continued. "I'm worried that Tom might try to hurt her so I am going to wait here."

"Tom won't hurt her." I said. "Tom isn't even thinking about Daisy. How long do you plan to wait?"

"I'll wait until they go to bed."

I stared at Daisy's house; there were three lighted windows downstairs. "Wait here for a minute," I said. "I'll go see if there's any trouble inside."

I walked silently through the yard and looked into the window.

Daisy and Tom were both sitting at the kitchen table; they were eating a plate of cold chicken and drinking two bottles of beer. Tom was talking, and sometimes Daisy nodded her head. They weren't happy and yet they didn't seem unhappy either. It looked like they were planning something together.

As I went back to tell Gatsby I heard my taxi coming.

"It's quiet there. Come back to West Egg and get some sleep."

"No, I'll wait until Daisy goes to bed. Good night, young fellow."

I got into the taxi and left Gatsby there watching the house, watching nothing.

来。我觉得我们撞到了那女人，便尽力使黛西停车，但她不愿停下来。"

"她明天就会好的，"他继续说。"我担心汤姆可能会伤害她，因此我要在这儿等着。"

"汤姆不会伤害她。"我说。"汤姆甚至不会想到会是黛西。你打算等多久？"

"我要等到他们去睡觉。"

我凝视着黛西的房子；楼下有三个窗户亮着灯。"你在这儿等一会儿。"我说。"我要去看看屋里是否有麻烦。"

我悄悄穿过院子，向窗子里望去。

黛西和汤姆都坐在厨房餐桌边；正吃着一盘凉鸡肉，喝着两瓶啤酒。汤姆正在说话，黛西偶尔点点头。他们不是很高兴但也看不出有什么不愉快，好像正在一起计划什么事。

我走回去告诉盖茨比，这时我听到我的出租车来了。

"那里很安静，回西卵镇睡会儿觉吧。"

"不，我要等到黛西去睡觉。晚安，老兄。"

我钻进出租车，留下盖茨比在那儿守望着那幢房子，白白守望着。

as [æz] *conj.* 引起时间状语从句，表示在某事发生的过程中另一事发生，意为"在…时候"。

177

CHAPTER NINE The Murder

That night I couldn't sleep. At about four in the morning I heard a taxi drive up to Gatsby's house. I immediately jumped out of bed and put on my clothes. I felt that I needed to talk to him before morning, that I had something to warn him about before it was too late.

I walked up to his house; his front door was still open. I found him sitting in the dining room.

"Nothing happened," he said. "I waited half the night. Finally she came to the window and stood there for a minute looking out. Then she turned off the light."

"You should leave," I said. "The police will find your car soon."

"Leave now?"

Gatsby explained that he *couldn't* possibly leave Daisy *until* he knew what she was going to do. Gatsby still hoped that Daisy would leave Tom and marry him, and I didn't want to tell him that there was no hope.

Gatsby then told me the story of his young life with Dan Cody on the sailing ship. He told me the story because he felt that "Jay Gatsby" was dead. Tom's hard strength had broken the idea of "Gatsby" like a piece of glass. The act of Jay Gatsby was over.

He told me about his young life with Daisy. She was the

第九章 谋 杀

那天晚上，我难以入眠。大约早晨四点钟时我听到一辆出租车开到盖茨比家。我立即从床上跳起来穿上衣服。我觉得天亮前我得跟他谈谈，我有话要提醒他，趁还来得及。

我走到他家，前门还开着，我发现他坐在餐厅里。

"什么事也没发生，"他说。"我等到半夜。最后她走到窗前，站在那儿往外看了一会儿，然后就关上灯。"

"你应该离开，"我说。"警察很快就会发现你的车。"

"现在离开？"

盖茨比解释说，他不可能离开黛西，直到他知道她打算怎么办。盖茨比仍然希望黛西会离开汤姆和他结婚，我不想告诉他这毫无希望。

接着，盖茨比告诉我他年轻时和丹·科迪在帆船上的事。他告诉我这个故事是因为他觉得"杰伊·盖茨比"已经死了。汤姆的强悍已经打碎了"盖茨比"那像玻璃一样的梦想。杰伊·盖茨比的行动已经结束了。

他告诉我他年轻时和黛西在一起的生活。

not until 直到…才。谓语通常为非持续性动词。如：Give him no definite answer until I've seen him. 我看到他后你再给他确切的答复。

179

first rich girl he had ever met. He thought that she was exciting and beautiful. He went over to her house, and it shocked him. He had never been inside such a big and beautiful house before. And because Daisy lived in the house, it *felt* magic inside.

But Gatsby had lied to Daisy. She did not know the real man. He had told her that he was very rich and powerful. He told her that he was able to take care of her. He even lied and said that he came from a wealthy family. The truth was that he was a poor young man without a good family or a past. When wearing his soldier's uniform nobody could know if he was rich or poor, but when the war was over, he would again become a poor nobody. So he decided to take everything that he could get — and in the end he took Daisy, one quiet October night.

He had planned to have fun for a while and then leave, but then he fell in love with Daisy. He could not leave her.

"I was surprised to find out that I loved her, young fellow. I hoped that she would leave me for a while, but she didn't, because she truly loved me." The day before he left for the war, he sat in Daisy's house with her *in his arms*. They sat for a long time together. They didn't talk, only sat and felt close to each other. They became calm and prepared to separate for a long time. They had only been in love for a month, but they felt that they would be in love forever.

Gatsby did very well in the war and even became a little

她是他曾遇到过的第一个富家女子，他认为她动人而美丽。去她家时他很震惊。他以前从来没进过这么大这么漂亮的房子。因为黛西住在这样的房子里，那里面就充满了魔力。

但是盖茨比对黛西撒了谎。她不知道他的真实情况。他告诉她他非常有钱有势。他告诉她他能够照顾她。他甚至谎称自己出身于一个富有的家庭。事实上他是一个没有富裕家庭，没有好背景的穷小子。穿上军装时没人知道他是富是穷，但当战争结束后，他又会变成一个可怜的无名小卒了。因此他决定要得到可能得到的一切——终于在十月里一个宁静的夜晚，他得到了黛西。

他本来打算玩一段时间，然后就离开，但后来他感觉他爱上了黛西，他离不开她了。

"老兄，我发现自己爱上她时，我很吃惊。我希望她离开我一段时间，但她没有，因为她真的爱上了我了。"去打仗的前一天，他拥着黛西坐在黛西家里。他们一块儿坐了很长时间，都不说话，只是坐着，彼此感觉很近。他们平静下来准备长久分离。他们只恋爱了一个月，但他们感觉他们会爱到永远。

盖茨比在战争中干得很不错，甚至小有

feel [fi:l] *vi.* 意为"感觉起来"，作连系动词。例如：1. Ice feels cold. 冰摸起来很凉。2. It felt pleasant to be going to work. 去上班感觉很好。

in one's arms 在某人的怀抱中；被某人拥抱着。

famous. He first became a captain and later increased to higher positions. After the war he wanted to go home and see Daisy, but the army sent him to Oxford instead. He became more and more worried by Daisy's letters. She wanted him to come home and didn't understand why he couldn't. She wanted him to be close to her; she wanted to know that he would take care of her and that he would be safe.

Daisy was young and she was feeling the pressure to get married. All of her friends were going out every night with men, but she stayed home waiting. Finally, in the spring, she began to go out again. Suddenly she was going out to meet a different man every night. She wanted to make a decision; she wanted her life to become safe and quiet immediately.

Then, in the middle of spring, Tom Buchanan met Daisy. He was strong, rich and had a good family, and he said that he would take care of Daisy. She felt relaxed letting him take care of her and she happily agreed to *marry* him. Gatsby received the letter announcing her marriage while he was still at Oxford.

"I don't think that Daisy ever loved Tom." Gatsby said. But when he sat down, his face didn't show any hope.

When Gatsby came back from France, Tom and Daisy were still on their wedding trip. He traveled to Louisville using the last of his money. For a whole week he went to the places that they had gone together and remembered the time that they spent together. He stayed until he had no more money, then he

名气。他先是成了上尉，后来又升为更高的军官。战后他想回家看黛西，但部队却把他送进了牛津大学。他被黛西的信弄得越来越心神不定。她想叫他回家，也不明白他为什么不能回家。她想叫他靠近她；她想知道他会照顾她，想知道他平安无事。

黛西很年轻，感受到了要出嫁的压力。她所有的朋友每天晚上都和男人们出去，而她却呆在家里等着。终于到了春天，她又开始出去了。突然之间她每晚都出去与不同的人约会。她想作个决定；她想要她的生活立即变得安全、宁静。

然后，在仲春时分，汤姆·布坎南遇见了黛西。他很强壮、富裕，家庭背景又好。并且他说他愿意照顾黛西。让他照顾她觉得轻松，她欣然同意嫁给他。接到她宣布要结婚的信时盖茨比仍在牛津。

"我不认为黛西曾经爱过汤姆。"盖茨比说。但当他坐下来时，他的脸上显示出毫无希望的神情。

盖茨比从法国回来后，汤姆和黛西仍在旅行结婚的途中。他到了路易斯维尔，花完了他最后一点钱。整整一个星期他走遍他们曾一块儿去过的地方，回忆他们一起度过的时光。他一直逗留到他没了钱，然后坐上公共汽车走

marry ['mæri] *v.*结婚。如：Mary is going to marry John. 玛丽要和约翰结婚了。

left on a bus.

We had talked for a long time, it was already nine o'clock and I had to leave soon to go to work. The gardener came outside and said, "Mr. Gatsby, I'm going to empty the pool today. The leaves will start falling soon, and they'll make the water dirty."

"Don't empty it today," Gatsby said. "I've still never used that pool. I think I will go in today."

I looked at my watch and stood up.

"I have to go to work." I said.

I didn't want to go to work that day, but, more than that, I didn't want to leave Gatsby. I talked with him for another hour, before I finally went to work.

"I'll call you during lunch," I said as I left.

"Please do, young fellow."

He walked with me down the stairs.

"I guess Daisy will call too." He looked at me nervously.

"Yes, I suppose she will." I had to lie to him.

"Goodbye Nick, thanks for coming over."

We shook hands and I left. Just before I got into my car I remembered something and turned around toward Gatsby.

"They're *no good*, any of them!" I yelled across the yard, and I meant Tom, Daisy, and all of the famous and fancy people who came to Gatsby's parties. "You are better than all of them added together!"

了。

我们谈了好长时间，已经九点了，我不得不快点离开去上班了。那个园丁来到门外说，"盖茨比先生，我打算今天清空游泳池。树叶很快就开始落了，会把水弄脏的。"

"今天别弄，"盖茨比说。"我还从来没用过这池子。我想今天用一次。"

我看看表，站了起来。

"我得上班了。"我说。

那天，我不想去上班，尤其是我不想离开盖茨比。我又跟他谈了一个小时，最后我才去上班。

"午饭时我给你打电话，"我边走边说。

"请一定打，老兄。"

他和我一起走下台阶。

"我猜黛西也会打电话的。"他紧张地看着我说。

"是的，我想她会的。"我不得不对他撒谎。

"再见，尼克，谢谢你能过来。"

握过手后我就离开了。我正要上车时忽然想起什么，我又转身向着盖茨比。

"他们不是好人，谁都不是！"我隔着院子叫道，我意指汤姆、黛西和所有那些来盖茨比家参加聚会的名人和时髦人物。"你比他们所有人加在一块儿还要好！"

no good 用于形容词前表示与该词相反的意思，"并不、并非、并无"。如：It is no easy task (no trivial matter). 这可不是一件容易的事（区区小事）。

Gatsby heard me and smiled his wonderful smile. I'm very happy that I said that to him. It was the only praise I ever said to Gatsby. In my heart I didn't agree with him or his life or his ideas.

In the office, I tried to work, but I fell asleep in my chair. The phone woke me. It was Jordan; she often called me at the office to see if I wanted to have lunch with her. Her voice usually sounded calm, but today it was *sharp* and angry.

"You weren't so nice to me last night." She said.

I became angry. "Last night, nothing was important."

She was silent for a minute. "I still want to see you."

"I want to see you, too."

"I could meet you in the city for lunch."

"Sorry, I have too much work this afternoon."

We talked in angry voices for a while, and then suddenly we weren't talking. I don't know who hung up and I didn't care. I was too angry to talk to her.

I called Gatsby, but there was no answer. I decided that I would leave work early, in about three hours.

I should go back now and tell a little about what happened at the garage after we left. The owner of the coffee shop, Michaelis, told this story later to the police.

Michaelis had waited with Wilson all night. Sometime after midnight the people in the garage left and Michaelis stayed there alone with Wilson. Wilson was still crying. Finally at

盖茨比听到我那样说，露出了他那美妙的笑容。我很高兴对他那样说。这是我对盖茨比说的惟一一句赞扬的话。在我心里我不赞同他、他的生活或想法。

在办公室里，我打算工作，但却倒在椅子里睡着了。电话铃吵醒了我。是乔丹，她经常打电话到我办公室看我是否想和她一块儿吃午饭。她的声音通常听起来很平静，但是今天却尖厉而愤怒。

"昨晚你对我不好。"她说。

我很生气。"昨晚，没什么重要的事。"

她沉默了一会儿。"我还是想见你。"

"我也想见你。"

"午饭时我可以在城里见你。"

"对不起，今天下午我还有很多工作要做。"

我们用生气的语气谈了一阵子，然后突然不谈了。我不知道是谁挂断了电话，我也不介意，我太生气了，无法跟她说话。

我打电话给盖茨比，但没人接。我决定早点下班，大约三小时后。

我现在应该回过头来，谈点儿我们离开车行以后那里发生的事。咖啡馆的老板米歇里斯后来跟警察讲了这个故事。

米歇里斯陪威尔逊等了一整夜。半夜过后的那段时间里车行的人都走了，只有米歇里斯待在那儿陪威尔逊。威尔逊还在哭。最后大约凌晨两点钟时他止住了哭，开始告诉米歇里

sharp [ʃɑːp] *adj.* 形容声音很尖，刺耳。a sharp voice 尖声。

about two in the morning he stopped crying, and he began to tell Michaelis stories about his wife.

First he told him that *a couple of* months before his wife had come home with her nose broken and bleeding.

"At that time I began to worry that something strange was happening. Then yesterday afternoon I discovered this piece of jewelry in her drawer." He then showed Michaelis what he found.

"She told me that her sister had given it to her, but I knew that she was lying — I realized then that she must have some young fellow in love with her." Wilson walked over to the window and looked outside. "I told her 'I don't know what you have been doing, but God knows. You can't hide from God's eyes — He sees everything! '"

"And then he murdered her," said Wilson.

"Who murdered her?"

"Her lover did! The man driving the big, yellow car! She ran outside to speak to him, but he wouldn't stop. He *drove over* her and murdered her! I'm going to find out who owns that yellow car."

By five o'clock in the morning Wilson had become quiet. Michaelis was very tired and went home to sleep. He told Wilson that he would come back to see him in the morning, but when he came back to the garage four hours later, Wilson was already gone.

斯他妻子的事。

他首先告诉他两个月前他妻子回家时，鼻子破了，还在流血。

"那时我就开始担心，怕有什么蹊跷的事发生。昨天下午我发现了她抽屉里的这件珠宝。"然后他把他发现的东西给米歇里斯看。

"她告诉我是她妹妹给的，但我看得出她在撒谎——于是我意识到一定有个家伙在跟她谈恋爱。"威尔逊走到窗边往外看。"我告诉她'我不知道你一直在干什么，但上帝知道，你逃不过上帝的眼睛——他能看到一切!'"

"然后他杀了她，"威尔逊说。
"谁杀了她?"

"她的情人杀的!那个开着黄色大轿车的人!她跑出去跟他说话，但他不愿停车。他从她身上轧过去，谋杀了她!我打算找出那辆黄车是谁的。"

凌晨五点钟时威尔逊平静了下来。米歇里斯很疲倦，就回家睡觉去了。他告诉威尔逊他上午再回来看他，但四个小时后当他回到车行时，威尔逊已经不见了。

a couple of 多用于口语，几个、二三个。
drive over（车）在…身上轧过去

189

Later the police learned where Wilson's had gone. First he walked to Gad's Hill. Many people saw him walking down the road and they said he looked a little bit crazy. At about twelve o'clock he reached Gad's Hill, and went in a restaurant to eat. For the next two hours he walked from garage to garage, looking for a big, yellow car. By two o'clock he arrived in West Egg; he asked someone on the street where Gatsby's house was. By that time he must have learned Gatsby's name.

According to one of his servants, Gatsby went out to the swimming pool at about two o'clock. He told his helper to tell him if the phone rang. He then went to the garage and told the driver not to use the car for any reason. The driver thought that this was strange, because the car was damaged *in the front* and it needed to be repaired.

Nobody called Gatsby that afternoon, not Daisy or anyone else. The helper waited near the phone until four o'clock. Sadly, this was long after there was anyone to receive a phone call. I don't think that Gatsby really believed that Daisy would call.

At about three o'clock his driver heard the sound of two gunshots, but he didn't know where they came from. No one had seen Gatsby for a few hours. It was not until I arrived home from work that we found Gatsby. I was worried that something was wrong and I ran over to his house and asked where he was. When I learned that he was in the pool, his driver, helper, gardener and I all ran down.

后来，警察了解到威尔逊去了哪儿。他先去了盖德山。许多人看见他沿路走着，他们说他看样子有点疯了。十二点钟左右他到了盖德山，然后进了一家饭店吃饭。随后的两个小时他从一家车行走到另一家车行，一直在找一辆黄色大轿车。两点钟时他到了西卵镇；他在街上打听盖茨比的家在哪儿。到那时他一定了解到了盖茨比的名字。

根据他的一个仆人的说法，盖茨比大约两点钟时去了游泳池。他告诉仆人如果电话铃响了就告诉他。然后他去车库告诉司机不管什么原因也别用那辆车了。司机想这很奇怪，因为汽车前面撞坏了，需要修。

那天下午不管是黛西还是别人都没有给盖茨比打电话。仆人在电话机旁一直等到四点。不幸的是，这离有人可接电话已有很长时间了。我想盖茨比不会真正相信黛西会给他打电话。

三点钟左右他的司机听到了两声枪响，但他不知道从哪儿传来的。好几个小时没看见盖茨比了，直到我下班回到家我们才发现盖茨比。我担心出了什么事，就跑到他家，问他在哪儿。当我得知他在游泳池里时，他的司机、仆人、园丁和我都跑过去。

in the front 一般作名词，但 in front of... 和 in the front of... 含义不同。前者意为"在…前面"，后者意为"在…的前部"。

The pool water was red with blood and Gatsby's body was slowly moving down the pool.

As we carried Gatsby's dead body towards the house the gardener saw Mr. Wilson's body dead in the grass. He had shot himself in the head.

游泳池里的水被血染红了，盖茨比的尸体正慢慢地往池底沉。

　　我们把盖茨比的尸体往屋子里抬时，园丁看见草地上威尔逊的尸体，他朝自己头上开了枪。

CHAPTER TEN The Great Gatsby

For the next two days a crowd of policemen, journalists and photographers filled Gatsby's house. They asked me many questions, but I said as little as possible. One policeman called Wilson "a crazy man" as he stared at his body that afternoon. The newspaper wrote these same words the next day.

Michaelis later told the police his story and they learned that Wilson had believed his wife was secretly sleeping with another man. I thought then that the police would learn about Tom's relationship with Mrs. Wilson, but her sister, Catherine, who could have told the police about Tom, didn't say a word. She told the police that her sister was very happy with her husband and had never seen Gatsby or anybody else. So, the police decided that Mrs. Wilson had been accidentally killed by a stranger; and that George Wilson, *crazy with sadness*, had found the owner of the car, shot him and then shot himself. The police were happy with this story and they left.

This business with the police wasn't important to me. *What was important* was that I realized that I was responsible for Gatsby, because no one else cared about him. I realized that I was *on Gatsby's side*, and that we were all alone.

From the moment I telephoned the news of the murder, journalist, policemen and neighbors asked me hundreds of

第十章　了不起的盖茨比

随后的两天里，一大群警察、记者和摄影师挤满了盖茨比的家。他们问了我许多问题，但我尽可能少说。那天下午当一个警察盯着威尔逊的尸体时，管他叫"疯子"，第二天的报纸上也用了这些同样的字眼。

米歇里斯后来把他的事告诉了警察，他们了解到威尔逊相信他的妻子暗地里和另一个男人同居。那时我想警察会知道汤姆和威尔逊太太的关系的，她妹妹凯瑟琳会跟警察说起汤姆的，但她只字未提。她告诉警察她姐姐和她丈夫很幸福，从未见过盖茨比和其他任何人。因此警察断定威尔逊太太被一个陌生人意外轧死；而乔治·威尔逊伤心得发狂，找到了车的主人就开枪杀了他，然后又开枪自杀。警察对这个故事很满意，就离开了。

警察们的这种公事对我并不重要。重要的是我意识到我要对盖茨比负责，因为没有别人关心他了。我意识到我站在盖茨比一边，并且我们都很孤独。

从我打电话报告谋杀的那一刻起，记者、警察和邻居们问了我几百个与他有关的问题。

be crazy with (sadness)（伤心）得发狂。

what was important... 由what引导的名词性从句作主语。意为"重要的是…"

on one's side 站在某人一边（支持某人）

195

questions about him. Nobody except me could answer these questions, because nobody else knew him.

A half an hour after we found Gatsby's body I called Daisy on the telephone. The servant told me that she and Tom had left early that afternoon and would not come back for many weeks.

"Where did they go?" I asked.

"I don't know. I can't say."

"Is there a way to call them?"

"No."

I wanted to find someone who loved Gatsby, so that he would not be as alone in death as he was in life. I called Meyer Wolfshiem on the telephone, but he wasn't in. Then I went into Gatsby's office and looked in his desk for the phone numbers of his parents or any other relatives, but I couldn't find any. The only thing I found in the desk was a picture of Dan Cody on his boat.

The next day I sent one of Gatsby's servants to New York with a letter to Meyer Wolfshiem, asking him to come out on the next train. I thought that he would definitely come anyway, when he saw the news in the morning newspaper; I was also sure that Daisy would soon call or write a letter. But Mr. Wolfshiem didn't come; instead he wrote a letter that said only, "Gatsby's death is a terrible shock to me, but I am busy with some business and do not want to be seen near Gatsby's body."

除了我，没人能回答这些问题，因为没有其他
人了解他。

在我们发现盖茨比的尸体半小时后，我
打电话给黛西。仆人告诉我她和汤姆那天下午
早早就离开了，许多星期都不会回来。

"他们去哪儿啦？"我问。

"我不知道。不好说。"

"有什么方法联络他们吗？"

"没有。"

我想找出喜欢盖茨比的什么人，不至于
让他死时跟活着时一样孤独。我打电话给迈
耶·沃尔夫山姆，但是他不在。然后我到盖茨
比的办公室从办公桌里翻找他父母或别的亲戚
的电话号码，但我一个也没找到。我能找到的
只有那个丹·科迪在船上的照片。

第二天我派盖茨比的一个仆人去纽约给
迈耶·沃尔夫山姆送封信，要他乘下一辆火车
过来。我想他看到早报上的新闻无论如何肯定
会来；我也确信黛西不久就会打电话或写信
来。但是沃尔夫山姆先生没来，而只写了这样
一封信："对盖茨比先生的死，我很受震惊，
但我正忙于一些业务，不想被别人看见我在盖
茨比的遗体旁。"

Later in the afternoon the phone rang, I thought that it would be Daisy, but I heard a man's voice on the phone.

"This is Slagle speaking..." the voice said.

"Yes?" I didn't know the name.

"Mr. Young is in trouble. The police caught him when he tried to sell those stolen *bank bonds*."

"Listen!" I interrupted. "I'm not Mr. Gatsby. Mr. Gatsby is dead."

The voice was silent for a long time and then it cried in fear and hung up suddenly.

On the third day after Gatsby's death, a letter arrived from Henry C. Gatz, Gatsby's father. It said that Mr. Gatz was coming immediately.

He came. He was a serious old man; he looked very tired and very sad.

"I read about it in the newspaper," he said. "The whole story was in the newspaper. So I came here at once."

"I wanted to find you, but I didn't know how." I said.

"A crazy man killed him," he said. "He must have been crazy."

"Would you like some coffee?" I asked.

"I don't want anything. I only want to see my son!"

I showed him the room where Gatsby lay, and left him there.

After a while he came out of the room; his mouth was

后来下午电话铃响了，我以为是黛西打来的，但我听到一个男人的声音。

"我是斯莱格……"那个声音说。

"谁?"我不知道这个名字。

"杨先生有麻烦了，在他试着卖掉那些偷来的银行债券时被警察抓住了。"

"听着!"我打断他的话。"我不是盖茨比先生，盖茨比先生死了。"

那个声音沉默了好长一阵子，然后惊恐地叫了一声，突然挂断了电话。

盖茨比死后的第三天，来了一封亨利·C·盖兹写的信，他是盖茨比的父亲。信上说盖兹先生马上就来。

他来了，他是一个非常严肃的老人，看上去很疲倦，也很悲伤。

"我从报纸上了解到这个消息的，"他说。"报纸上登了整个经过。因此我立刻就来了。"

"我想找到你们，但我不知怎么找。"我说。

"一个疯子杀了他，"他说。"他一定是疯了。"

"想喝点咖啡吗?"我问。

"我什么也不想要，我只想看看我的儿子!"

我把他领到他儿子躺着的屋子，把他留在那儿。

过了一会儿，他从屋里出来;嘴张着，

bank bonds 银行债券

199

open, and tears were falling down his face. He was an old man and death was no longer a terrible surprise to him. He began to look around the room and when he saw the fancy house and all the expensive things in the hall and huge rooms, his sadness began to be *mixed with* pride. I showed him a bedroom where he could rest, and told him that the arrangements for the funeral had been stopped until he arrived.

"I thought you might want to take his body back to the West, Mr. Gatsby — "

"My name is Gatz," he said sadly. He then shook his head. "My son liked the East better than the West. This is where he became rich and famous. Were you a good friend of his?"

"Yes, we were close friends."

"My son had a great future in front of him, you know. He would have been a great man if he had lived. He would have helped develop this country."

"That's true," I said, but I knew it wasn't true.

Mr. Gatz lay down, and immediately fell asleep.

Mr. Klipspringer, the young man who had been Gatsby's houseguest for so long, called on the phone. I was glad because I thought he would also come to the funeral. Then Gatsby would have another friend at his grave.

"The funeral is tomorrow," I told him. "At the house at two o'clock, please tell anybody who'd be interested. I would

了不起的盖茨比

泪流满面。他是一个老人，死亡对于他已不再恐怖惊人。他开始环视屋子，当他看见这漂亮的房子和大厅里、大房间里所有昂贵的物品时，他的悲伤开始掺进了自豪。我带他到一间他可以休息的卧室，告诉他葬礼的安排停下来了，只等他来。

"我想您可能要把他的尸体带回到西部去，盖茨比先生——"

"我姓盖兹。"他难过地说，然后又摇摇头。"我儿子喜欢东部胜过西部。这是他变富成名的地方。你是他的好朋友吗?"

"是的，我们是好朋友。"

"我儿子是大有前程的，你知道。如果他活着他会成为了不起的人。他会帮助这个国家发展的。"

"没错，"我说，但我知道这不可能。

盖兹先生躺下，很快睡着了。

克利普斯普林格先生，做了盖茨比先生好长时间房客的那个年轻人，打电话过来了。我很高兴，因为我以为他也会来参加葬礼，这样盖茨比的墓前又多了一位朋友。

"葬礼安排在明天，"我告诉他。"两点钟时就在家里，请转告任何想来的人。我想打

mix with 混同，这里意思是痛苦中夹杂着对儿子的自豪感。

201

call people, but I don't know who his friends were. Of course, you'll be there."

"Well, actually, I don't think I can come. I, ah, just called because I left a pair of shoes there. Could you ask one of the servants to send them to me? My address is — "

I was so angry that I *hung up* the phone before he could say his address.

The morning before the funeral I went to see Meyer Wolfshiem. He brought me into his office and gave me a cigar. He told me that he felt very sad about Gatsby's death.

" I can still remember when I first met him," he said. "He was young and had just come back from the war. He was looking for work.I remember that he was so poor that he was still wearing his army uniform because he couldn't afford to buy some common clothes.He hadn't eaten for two days when I saw him.I took him to lunch and he ate more than four dollars' of food in half an hour."

"Did you give him a job?" I asked.

"Give him a job! I made him rich! He had nothing and I gave him everything. He looked like a gentleman, and when he told me he went to Oxford I knew I could use him. He first worked for a friend of mine and we quickly became very close friends," — Wolfshiem held up two of his fat fingers — "we were always together."

"He's dead now," I said after a moment. "You were his

电话给他们，可我不知道他的朋友是谁。当然，你会来的。"

"哦，其实，我想我不能来了。我，噢，打电话是因为我落了一双鞋在那儿。你能叫他的仆人给我寄过来吗?我的地址是——"

我很生气，还没等说他出地址，我就挂断了电话。

葬礼前的那天早晨我去看迈耶·沃尔夫山姆，他把我带到他的办公室并给了我一支雪茄，他告诉我他对盖茨比的死非常悲伤。

"我仍能记起我第一次见他的情景，"他说。"他很年轻，刚从战场上归来。他正在找工作。我记得他很穷，仍然穿着军装，因为他买不起便服。我看见他时，他已两天没吃饭了。我带他去吃午饭，他竟半小时内吃了四美元多的食物。"

"是你给了他工作吗?"我问。

"给他工作!我使他富起来了!他什么也没有，而我给了他一切。他看上去像个绅士，当他告诉我他上过牛津时，我知道我可以任用他。他先为我的一个朋友工作，我们很快成了很亲密的朋友，"——沃尔夫山姆举起他的两根粗指头——"我们总是在一起。"

"现在他死了，"过了一会儿我说。"你

best friend, so you should come to his funeral today."

"Sorry, I can't. I can't be seen near him," he said. "In my business it is best to stay away from a man who's been killed."

I went back to West Egg, *changed into* my best clothes and went to the funeral. It was raining and dark. Mr. Gatz was walking around the house excitedly. His pride in his son's wealth was increasing.

"When did you last see your son?" I asked.

"He came to see me two years ago, and he bought me the house where I live now. He was always very kind to me."

Before the man from the church arrived, I began to look outside for any cars. The servants all came and Mr. Gatz and I, and we all waited in the hall. I asked the man from the church to wait for an hour for the other guests. But there was no reason, nobody else came.

After the funeral we drove out to the graveyard. As we carried Gatsby's body towards the grave I heard a car stop. I turned around and saw the man with the round glasses whom I had met in Gatsby's library during the first party I went to.

I'd never seen that man since then and I don't know how he learned about the funeral.

"Sorry, I couldn't get to the house," he said.

"Nobody else could either." I said with my head down.

" Really! They used to go to his house *by the hun-*

是他最好的朋友，因此你今天应该参加他的葬礼。"

"对不起，我不能去。不能被别人看见我在他旁边，"他说。"我的生意让我最好远离一个被谋杀的人。"

我回到西卵镇，换上我最好的衣服去参加葬礼。天正下着雨，阴沉沉的。盖兹先生在屋里激动地走来走去，他对他儿子的财富所感到的自豪感正在不断增长。

"你最后一次见到你儿子是什么时候？"我问。

"两年前他来看过我，给我买了我现在住的房子。他一直对我很好。"

在教堂的人到来之前，我开始往外看，寻找一些汽车。仆人们全都来了，还有盖兹先生和我，大家都在大厅里等着。我叫教堂的人等一个小时，再等等别的客人。但毫无用处，没有别人来了。

葬礼后我们驱车去墓地，当我们把盖茨比的尸体抬向坟墓时，我听到一辆车停了下来。我转过身，看见一个戴着圆眼镜的男人，我第一次去盖茨比家参加聚会时在他家的书房里见过这个人。

从那以后我再没见过他，我不知道他是怎么知道这个葬礼的。

"对不起，我没能赶到他家，"他说。
"别人也没去。"我低着头说。

"真的！他们曾经成百成百地去他家呀！"

change into 换（衣）。例如：
You must change into a clean dress before going out. 你外出前必须换上一套干净的衣服。

by the hundreds = by hundreds 数以百计地，大批地。

205

dreds!" The rain fell down his face and round glasses. He took his glasses off and we watch Gatsby being put into the earth.

I tried to remember Gatsby for a moment, but he already felt very far away. The only thing I could think about was that Daisy hadn't even sent a letter or flowers.

I understand now that my story of the East has really been about the West. Tom and Gatsby, Daisy and Jordan and I, were all born in the West. Perhaps we all had the same deep problem inside which made us unable to live in the East.

After Gatsby died I stopped liking the East. In October I left New York and came back home.

There was only one thing I still had to do before I left for the West. I went and saw Jordan Baker, and I talked about our relationship, and about how I had changed in the end. She sat in a big chair and was silent. When I finished speaking she told me that she was about to marry another man. I did not *believe* her, I thought that she was only saying it to make me angry, but I pretended to be surprised.

"But you were the one who left me," said Jordan. "You hung up on me on the telephone before. I don't care about you anymore, but it was a new experience for me, no man has ever left me before. For a while it made me feel a little strange."

I stood up and said goodbye and we shook hands.

"Do you remember," she said, "a conversation we had

雨水沿着他的脸上和圆眼镜片流下来。他摘下眼镜，我们看着盖茨比入土。

有那么一会儿，我尽力想记起盖茨比，但感觉他已太遥远了。我惟一能想到的就是黛西连一封信或一些花都没送来。

我现在明白了，我在东部的故事，实际上是关于西部的故事。汤姆、盖茨比、黛西、乔丹和我，都出生在西部。也许我们大家心里都有同样的深层次问题，这使我们不能生活在东部。

盖茨比死后我不再喜欢东部了，十月份我离开纽约回到了家乡。

回西部之前我仍有惟一一件事得做。我去看乔丹·贝克，我谈了我俩的关系以及最后我是怎样改变的。她坐在大椅子里，沉默着。我说完后，她告诉我她打算嫁给另一个男人。我不相信她的话，我以为她这样说只是想让我生气，但我还是假装很吃惊。

"不过，是你甩掉我的"乔丹说。"以前打电话时你挂断了我的电话，我不再在意你了，但这对我来说是段新经历，以前没人甩过我。有一阵子这使我觉得有点奇怪。"

我站起来道别，然后我俩握了握手。

"你还记得我们以前关于开车的一次谈话

believe [bi'li:v] *v.* 注意不要混淆 believe sb. 与 believe in sb. 的含义。前者是"相信某人（的话）"；后者是"信赖、信任某人（人格、为人方面）"，试比较：1. You can ask you father if you don't believe me. 你如果不信的话，可以去问你父亲。2. She used to believe in me. 她过去一直信任我。

207

once about driving a car? You said that a careless driver was only safe until she met another careless driver. Well, I met one, didn't I? I was wrong about you. I thought you were an honest person, but you are as careless as I am."

What she said made me feel angry and half in love with her, and very sorry that we had ended this way; I walked away.

Just before I left I saw Tom Buchanan in the city. He was walking in the city and when he saw me he walked over to me holding out his hand, but I did not move.

"What's the problem, Nick? Do you refuse to shake hands with me?"

"Yes. You know what I think about you, Tom." Then I asked him, "What did you say to Wilson that afternoon before he killed Gatsby?"

He stared at me and didn't speak, and I knew that I had guessed the truth. Tom had told Wilson that Gatsby had killed his wife. I started to *turn away from* Tom, but he grasped my arm and stopped me.

"I told Wilson the truth," he said. "He came to my door while we were preparing to leave. I told the servant to say we were away, but he *forced his way* inside. He was acting crazy and he had a gun. He might have killed me if I hadn't told him who owned the car." Tom then paused for a moment. "Gatsby should have died anyway. He drove over my girlfriend like you'd drive over a dog. He never even stopped his car."

吗?"她说，"你说过一个粗心的司机只有在遇到另一个粗心的司机之前她才是安全的。那么，我就遇到了一个，不是吗?我看错了你。我以为你是一个诚实的人，但你和我一样不负责任。"

她的话让我生气，又对她半含爱恋，也使我感觉这样结束很令人伤心；我走了。

就在我离开之前我在城里看见了汤姆·布坎南。他在城里走着，看见我时他走过来伸出手，但我没动。

"怎么了，尼克?你拒绝和我握手吗?"

"是的，你知道我怎么看你，汤姆。"然后我问他，"那天下午在威尔逊杀死盖茨比之前你跟他说了什么?"

他盯着我没说话，我知道我已猜出了真相。汤姆已经告诉威尔逊是盖茨比杀了他的妻子。我刚要转身离去，但汤姆抓住我的胳膊，挡住了我。

"我告诉威尔逊的是实情，"他说。"当我们正准备离开时，他来到我家门前。我告诉仆人说我们已经走了，但他硬闯了进来。他像疯了一样，带着枪。如果我不告诉他那车是谁的，他或许会杀了我的。"然后汤姆停了一会儿。"盖茨比无论如何都该死。他轧死我的女友就像轧死一条狗一样，他甚至连车都没停。"

turn away from... 从⋯离开、走开、出发。
force his way 强行前进或进入。例如：This army forced its way northward. 这个部队强行向北推进。

209

There was nothing I could say to him. I couldn't tell him that *it was* really Daisy *who* killed Mrs. Wilson.

I couldn't forgive Tom or like him, but I understood that he believed that he had done the right thing. He was careless and stupid. Tom and Daisy were careless people, they destroyed things and hurt people, and then made other people fix the damage that they caused. In the end they could always hide in their money, or their carelessness, or whatever power it was that kept them together.

I shook his hand; it felt silly not to, for I suddenly realized that I was talking to a child in an adult body.

When I finally left West Egg Gatsby's huge house was still empty — the grass on his yard was as long as my grass.

On my last night in West Egg, I went over and looked once last time at Gatsby's huge house. Then I walked down on to Gatsby's piece of beach and sat on the sand. As I sat there thinking, I thought of the wonder in Gatsby's heart when he first saw the green light on Daisy's wall. He had traveled a long way to this place, and Daisy seemed so close to him that he was sure he would have her again. He did not understand that Daisy was already in his past; their time together was still somewhere far outside of the city, somewhere in the Midwest where a young Daisy and a young Jay Gatsby were still in love.

Gatsby believed in his dream of a future with Daisy. He didn't realize that when we move towards our dreams, they

我什么也不能对他说。我不能告诉他事实上是黛西轧死了威尔逊太太。

　　我不能原谅汤姆，也不可能喜欢他，但我知道他相信自己做得对。他很不负责任，也很愚蠢。汤姆和黛西都是不负责任的人，他们毁坏东西，伤害人，然后让别人来修补他们造成的残局。最后他们总是隐藏到他们的金钱、他们的无所谓或任何能让他们待在一起的力量里去。

　　我握了握他的手；如果不握我觉得愚蠢，因为我突然意识到我正在跟一个长着成人身躯的小孩说话。

　　我最后离开西卵镇时，盖茨比的大房子还空着——院子里的草长得和我院子里的草一样高了。

　　在西卵镇的最后一个晚上，我过去最后再看一次盖茨比的大房子。然后我走到盖茨比家的那片海滩上，坐在沙滩上。我坐在那儿思考着，我想到了当盖茨比第一次看到黛西家堤上的那盏绿灯时他心中的惊奇。他走了这么远的路来到这个地方，黛西看起来离他如此之近，使他确信自己能再次得到她。他不明白黛西已经成为他的过去；他们在一块儿的时光仍远在这个城市之外的某个地方，在中西部年轻的黛西和年轻的杰伊·盖茨比仍在热恋中的某个地方。

　　盖茨比相信他和黛西的未来之梦。他没有意识到当我们朝着梦想追求时，它们却离我们

it is... who 这是一个强调句型。如果我们想要强调某个词或某个短语，句子可以用it is或it was+主语+that或who(m)来开头，这样组成的句子叫做分裂句。如：It was Freda who phoned Jack last night. 昨晚，是佛雷达给杰克打的电话。

211

move farther and farther away from us. We move forward, like boats sailing against the wind and the waves, but all the time we are carried back into our past.

们越来越远了。我们像航船逆风逆浪而行一样前进，但我们却一直被拉回到我们往昔的岁月中。

床头灯英语学习读本

Ⅰ.《查泰莱夫人的情人》

《飘》

《红与黑》

《了不起的盖茨比》

《歌剧魅影》

《三个火枪手》

《傲慢与偏见》

《呼啸山庄》

《简·爱》

《儿子与情人》

Ⅱ.《鲁滨逊漂流记》

《大战火星人》

《巴斯克维尔猎犬》

《时间机器》

《远大前程》

《彼得·潘》

《格列佛游记》

《黑骏马》

《汤姆·索亚历险记》

《杨柳风》

Ⅲ.《德伯家的苔丝》

《化身博士》

《野性的呼唤》

《阿丽思漫游奇境记》

《弗兰肯斯坦》

《白鲸》

《环游地球 80 天》

《圣诞欢歌》

《圣经故事》

《希腊神话故事》

考试虫丛书学术委员会

推 荐 书 目

书名　介绍	版　　别	定价
考试虫系列－大学英语四、六级考试		
大学英语四级考试 辅导讲义 　　四级考试一本通。	航空工业	25.00
大学英语四级考试 辅导讲义(音带2盒)	开明文教	14.00
英语词汇速听速记手册—1－4级词汇掌中宝	航空工业	8.00
(盒装)英语词汇速听速记手册—1－4级词汇掌中宝 (1书3带)	开明文教	29.00
英语词汇速听速记手册—1－6级词汇掌中宝	航空工业	8.00
(盒装)英语词汇速听速记手册—1－6级词汇掌中宝 (1书4带)	开明文教	36.00
磨耳朵——大学英语四级词汇(书1本音带5盒)	开明文教	36.00
磨耳朵——大学英语六级词汇(书1本音带2盒)	开明文教	17.00
大学英语1－4级词汇手边书(新) 　　书不大,信息含量高,建议同学们将此书读16～ 25遍。	航空工业	12.80
大学英语5－6级词汇手边书(新)	航空工业	8.80
大学英语四级词汇串讲 　　详略得当,快速串讲。	航空工业	15.00
大学英语六级词汇串讲	航空工业	19.00
大学英语1～4级词汇记忆考点札记 　　记忆＋考点	航空工业	25.00
大学英语5～6级词汇记忆考点札记	航空工业	13.00

书名 介绍	版 别	定价
大学英语四级考试四会式词汇	航空工业	13.00
大学英语四级词汇"考试虫"记忆树	航空工业	15.00
大学英语六级词汇"考试虫"记忆树	航空工业	16.00
大学英语四级考试 听力高分有术 　　听力技巧专著,是听力应试最高境界的体现。	航空工业	10.00
大学英语四级考试 听力高分有术(音带3盒)	开明文教	21.00
大学英语六级考试 听力高分有术	航空工业	10.00
大学英语六级考试 听力高分有术(音带3盒)	开明文教	21.00
大学英语四、六级考试 听力高分有术	航空工业	17.00
大学英语四、六级考试 听力高分有术(音带4盒)	开明文教	28.00
大学英语四、六级考试 听力高分有术(精华版) **(书1本,音带2盒)** 　　精选了《大学英语四、六级考试听力高分有术》书中部分精华内容,并配2盒音带。	开明文教	20.00
大学英语四、六级考试 万能作文 　　本书采用万能写作模式,使考生能在最短时间内提高自己的英语写作水平。	航空工业	12.00
大学英语四、六级考试 万能作文(背诵版) 　　精选了《大学英语四、六级考试万能作文》中范文,并配上录音,使你可以闭着眼睛背作文。	开明文教	8.00
大学英语阅读基本功——难句过关 　　如果把难句都掰扯明白了,那阅读不就过关了嘛!	航空工业	12.00
大学英语阅读基本功——难句过关(1书3带)	北京电视 艺术中心	33.00
大学英语四级考试 阅读手记 　　阅读技巧专著,被誉为"四级阅读冲刺第一书"。	航空工业	18.00

书 名 介 绍	版 别	定价
大学英语六级考试 阅读手记	航空工业	22.00
大学英语语法考点手册 　　专门把四级语法考点提炼出来,重点突出,针对性强。适合四级考试有 40 或 50 分实力的人使用。	航空工业	12.00
最新大学英语语法考点	航空工业	12.00
大学英语四级考试 听力模拟题与精听训练 (书 1 本,音带 3 盒) 　　八套题,清华大学黄淑琳教授主编	开明文教	26.00
大学英语四级考试"考试虫"试卷	航空工业	12.00
大学英语四级考试 "考试虫"试卷(音带 3 盒)	开明文教	21.00
大学英语六级考试"考试虫"试卷	航空工业	12.00
大学英语六级考试 "考试虫"试卷(音带 3 盒)	开明文教	21.00
大学英语四级考试冲刺试卷(其中 8 套试题 7.00 元)	航空工业	12.00
大学英语四级考试冲刺试卷(音带 2 盒)	开明文教	14.00
大学英语四级考试全题型模拟题精解(二)(其中 10 套试卷 8.00 元,教案 14.80 元) 　　十套题,解答详尽。	航空工业	22.80
大学英语四级考试全题型模拟题精解(二)(音带 3 盒)	开明文教	21.00
大学英语四级考试优化训练试卷 　　本书试题的命制由命题、初审、预测、试卷项目分析、审题和构卷等多个流程完成,具有很高的信度、效度和很强的科学性。	航空工业	15.00
大学英语四级考试优化训练试卷(音带 3 盒)	开明文教	21.00

书名　介绍	版　别	定价
最新大学英语考试题库精解(四级)(其中 10 套试卷 10.00 元) 　　十套题,试题活页分装,解答详尽。可方便教师备课。	航空工业	29.00
最新大学英语考试题库精解(四级)(音带 3 盒)	开明文教	21.00
洞穿四级——大学英语四级考试历年实考试题解析 　　最新 10 套全真题、全译本	航空工业	13.80
洞穿四级——大学英语四级考试历年实考试题解析 (音带 3 盒)	开明文教	21.00
洞穿六级——大学英语六级考试历年实考试题解析 　　最新 10 套全真题、全译本	航空工业	13.80
洞穿六级——大学英语六级考试历年实考试题解析 (音带 3 盒)	开明文教	21.00
大学英语历年实考试题解析(四级) 　　最新 15 套(合适的考前训练量)全真题及精解,如果把 15 套全真题都弄懂,那四级也就过关了。	航空工业	20.00
大学英语历年实考试题解析(四级)(音带 4 盒)	开明文教	28.00
大学英语历年实考试题解析(六级) 　　最新 15 套(合适的考前训练量)全真题及精解,如果把 15 套全真题都弄懂,那六级也就过关了。	航空工业	20.00
大学英语历年实考试题解析(六级)(音带 4 盒)	开明文教	28.00
考试虫系列－考研:		
英语词汇速听速记手册—考研词汇掌中宝	航空工业	8.00
(盒装)英语词汇速听速记手册—考研词汇掌中宝(1书 4 带) 　　所有英文词条都配有录音,标准美音,由中央台合成。	开明文教	36.00

书名　介绍	版　别	定价
磨耳朵——考研英语听力词汇(1 书 4 带) 　　所有英文词条和例句都有录音,建议听 16～25 遍,打通耳关。	北京电视 艺术中心	36.00
硕士研究生入学考试英语四会式词汇	航空工业	15.00
硕士研究生入学考试英语词汇"考试虫"记忆树	航空工业	20.00
MBA 联考英语词汇掌中宝	北京电视 艺术中心	8.00
MBA 联考英语词汇掌中宝(音带 4 盒)	北京电视 艺术中心	28.00
MBA 联考英语词汇掌中宝(1 书 4 带)	北京电视 艺术中心	36.00
工商管理硕士入学考试 MBA 万能作文(英语) 　　单句写作与篇章写作相结合;万能模式写作与自由写作相结合;两周背下万能模板,胜过考前苦读百篇作文。	航空工业	20.00
硕士研究生入学考试 英语听力模拟题与精听训练(书 1 本,音带 3 盒) 　　清华大学黄淑琳教授精心命制的 8 套考研听力模拟题与精听训练。	开明文教	26.00
硕士研究生入学考试 英语辅导讲义 　　本书由北大毕金献教授对考研命题的深刻理解和"考试虫"总主编王若平博士对英语考试的切身体会及"考试虫"学习体系教授团队呕心沥血的工作融合而成。	航空工业	42.00
硕士研究生入学考试 英语辅导讲义(音带 2 盒)	开明文教	14.00
考研英语听力基本功——听写训练①～④(书 1 本,音带 2 盒) 　　听写训练是提高听力的必由之路。如果您真想提高听力,就静下心来,踏踏实实地练习听写。	开明文教	17.00

书名　介绍	版　别	定价
硕士研究生英语入学考试 阅读基本功(难句过关) 　　如果把难句都掰扯明白了,那阅读不就过关了嘛!	航空工业	20.00
硕士研究生英语入学考试 阅读基本功(难句过关)(1 书3带)	北京电视 艺术中心	41.00
硕士研究生英语入学考试 阅读手记 　　阅读技巧专著,被誉为"考研阅读冲刺第一书"。	航空工业	25.00
硕士研究生英语入学考试 万能作文 　　采用万能模式,使考生能在最短时间内提高自己 的考试应试水平。"两周背下万能模式,胜过考前苦 读百篇作文。"	航空工业	20.00
硕士研究生英语入学考试 万能作文(背诵版) 　　精选了《硕士研究生英语入学考试万能作文》中 范文,并配上录音,使你可以闭着眼睛背作文。	开明文教	10.00
洞穿考研——硕士研究生英语入学考试历年实考试 题解析 　　帮助考生从历年实考试题中吸取精华;答题的最 高境界是再现。	航空工业	39.00
洞穿考研——硕士研究生英语入学考试历年实考试 题解析(音带2盒)	开明文教	14.00
硕士研究生英语入学考试 词汇记忆考点札记 　　本书编写历时两载,浓缩:记忆＋考点。	航空工业	17.00
洞穿考研数学(理工类) 　　最贴近考生需求的考研数学书,实用性强。	航空工业	44.00
洞穿考研数学(经济类)	航空工业	39.00
硕士研究生入学考试 陈先奎政治8套模拟试卷 　　山不在高,有仙则名;题不在多,有陈先奎押题则灵。	航空工业	13.00
陈先奎政治考前串讲讲义 　　听过陈先奎课的人都领教过他串讲和押题的功 夫,您该试试。	航空工业	20.00

书名　介绍	版　别	定价
硕士研究生入学考试"考试虫"英语 8 套模拟试卷 　　主编：毕金献(原教育部考研英语命题组组长)，王若平(考试虫)	航空工业	13.00
硕士研究生入学考试"考试虫"英语 8 套模拟试卷(音带 3 盒)	开明文教	21.00
硕士研究生入学考试"考试虫"数学(数 1、2、3、4)8 套模拟试卷 　　主编　原教育部考研数学资深命题人员：范培华教授(1987—2001 年命题)，李恒沛教授(1987—2001年命题)，胡金德教授(1989—1997 年命题)，王式安教授(1987—2001 年命题)，周概容教授(1987—2003 年命题)。可以说，他们对考研数学命题绝对有最深刻、最权威的把握。	航空工业	10.00 (估)/册
考研数学基础教程 　　本书助考生在命题人员的指导下进行三基训练，书中所用试题质量很高，包含历年备选试题及阅卷过程中发现考生容易出错的试题。	航空工业	39.00
洞穿考研医学 　　历年实考试题精析。	航空工业	36.00
考研西医综合核心笔记 　　精炼考研西医综合内容，把生理、生化、病理、内科、外科 5 本书变成了 1 本书，助考生快捷、安全过关。	航空工业	32.00
硕士研究生政治入学考试哲学、政经重难点分析 　　最难啃的骨头要先啃	航空工业	15.00
硕士研究生政治入学考试政治辅导讲义	航空工业	40.00
硕士研究生政治入学考试政治核心试题	航空工业	30.00
硕士研究生政治入学考试形势与政策及核心试题增编	航空工业	15.00
硕士研究生政治入学考试政治考前 50 题	航空工业	12.00
同等学力人员申请硕士学位英语水平全国统一考试专家点评	航空工业	16.80

书名 介绍	版 别	定价
同等学力人员申请硕士学位英语水平全国统一考试专家点评(音带3盒)	开明文教	21.00
同等学力人员申请硕士学位英语统考应试指南(修订三版) 　　本书作者对同等学力人员申请硕士学位英语统考有深入研究是一本金牌书。	航空工业	34.00
同等学力人员申请硕士学位英语统考应试指南(音带4盒)	开明文教	28.00
考试虫系列－自学考试：		
自考词汇掌中宝 　　先听、再说、后写是人类学习语言的本能，是记忆单词、增强语感最朴实的方法。	开明文教	8.00
自考词汇掌中宝(音带4盒) 　　所有英文词条都配有录音，标准美音，由中央台合成。	开明文教	28.00
(盒装)自考词汇掌中宝(1书4带)	开明文教	36.00
美国播音员教你读课文 　　美国播音员教你读《大学英语自学教程》上册A篇生词及课文　慢速	北京电视艺术中心	25.00
考试虫系列－大学英语学习与考试：		
大学新生入学英语衔接丛书——听力① 　　试题12套,难度:一级,选材新,趣味性强,解答详尽。	开明文教	10.00
大学新生入学英语衔接丛书——听力①(音带4盒) 　　录音语速较慢，语音标准（美音）、清楚，由中央台合成。	开明文教	28.00
大学新生入学英语衔接丛书——听力② 　　试题12套,难度:二级,选材新,趣味性强,解答详尽。	开明文教	10.00

书名　介绍	版　别	定价
大学新生入学英语衔接丛书——听力②(音带4盒) 　　录音语速较慢，语音标准（美音）、清楚，由中央台合成。	开明文教	28.00
大学新生入学英语衔接丛书——阅读① 　　80篇文章，每篇文章均按四级考试阅读模式出题，难度一级，选材好，趣味性强，解答详尽。	航空工业	15.00
大学新生入学英语衔接丛书——阅读② 　　80篇文章，每篇文章均按四级考试阅读模式出题，难度二级，选材好，趣味性强，解答详尽。	航空工业	15.00
英语词汇速听速记手册——《新编大学英语》词汇掌中宝 　　是《新编大学英语》教材的词汇本。	开明文教	8.00
英语词汇速听速记手册——《新编大学英语》词汇掌中宝(音带4盒) 　　所有英文词条都配有录音，标准美音，由中央台合成。	开明文教	28.00
英语词汇速听速记手册——《大学英语·精读》 **(1—4册)词汇掌中宝** 　　是《大学英语·精读》教材的词汇本。	开明文教	4.00
英语词汇速听速记手册——《大学英语·精读》 **(1—4册)词汇掌中宝**(音带2盒)	开明文教	14.00
《大学英语·精读》词汇记忆考点札记 　　记忆＋考点	航空工业	18.00
钻研《大学英语·精读》①～④ 　　本书对《大学英语·精读》课文进行逐字逐句的精炼讲解，使您轻松彻底弄懂课文。	航空工业	12.00/册
英语词汇速听速记手册——《新概念英语》(1—4册) **词汇掌中宝** 　　《新概念英语》教材的词汇本。	航空工业	4.00

书名　介绍	版　别	定价
英语词汇速听速记手册——《**新概念英语**》(1－4 册) 词汇掌中宝(音带 2 盒)	开明文教	14.00
(**盒装**)**英语词汇速听速记手册**——《**新概念英语**》 (1－4 册)词汇掌中宝(音带 2 盒)	开明文教	18.00
钻研《新概念英语》①～④ 　　谨以此书献给那些英语学了多年,却没有入门的 同学;那些在中高级英语考试中屡战屡败,屡败屡战 并试图通过英语来改变自身命运的人;那些曾经学过 英语,但已丢了多年,想重新开始学英语的人。	航空工业	23.00/册
《**新编大学英语**》①～③**示范教案**	航空工业	15.00/册
《**新编大学英语**》④**示范教案**	航空工业	17.00
《**新编大学英语**》①～④**词汇记忆考点札记**	航空工业	12.00/册
教你学《21 世纪大学英语·读写教程》①～④	航空工业	12.00/册
大学英语循序渐进听力训练 1(书 1 本,音带 3 盒) 　　本书是以"听力不可能速成"为指导思想,根据大 学英语教学和考试大纲编写的一套循序渐进的英语 精听教材。一级:句子填空,单词听辨,对话听辨等。	开明文教	26.00
大学英语循序渐进听力训练 2(书 1 本,音带 3 盒) 　　二级:句子听写,对话听辨,段落听辨等。	开明文教	26.00
大学英语循序渐进听力训练 3(书 1 本,音带 3 盒) 　　三级:句子及复合听写,对话听辨(十大主题),段 落听辨等。	开明文教	26.00
大学英语循序渐进听力训练 4(书 1 本,音带 3 盒) 　　四级:对话听辨,复合听写,段落听辨(标准四级 考试题型)。	开明文教	26.00

书名　介绍	版　别	定价
大学英语三级听力全题型训练 　　试题 12 套,难度:大英三级,选材新,趣味性强,解答详尽,录音语速较慢,语音标准(美音)、清楚,由中央台合成。	航空工业	12.00
大学英语三级听力全题型训练(音带 4 盒)	北京电视 艺术中心	28.00
英语词汇速听速记手册——常用口语词汇掌中宝	开明文教	4.00
英语词汇速听速记手册——常用口语词汇掌中宝(音带 2 盒)	开明文教	14.00
(盒装)英语词汇速听速记手册——常用口语词汇掌中宝(1 书 2 带)	开明文教	18.00
大学英语词汇讲座和练习 　　本书最大的特点是滴水不漏,覆盖了四、六级考试词汇的所有测试点。如果你把这本书读透了,词汇题就没有不会做的。	航空工业	18.00
大学英语语法讲座和练习(修订五版) 　　语法是成年人学英语的捷径。本书对英语的语法进行了全面讲解,其练习设计尤为实用。	航空工业	21.00
大学英语写作讲座和练习(修订三版)	兵器工业	8.50
洞穿雅思—雅思考试真题分析与实练 　　最贴近考生需求,实用性强。	航空工业	20.00
床头灯英语学习读本 I: 　　三千词读遍天下书。 　　喜欢读有趣的故事、小说是人类的天性。这套读物使得你不用翻字典,躺在床上就可以津津有味地学英语,把长期的、艰苦的英语学习变成一件有意思的事情,不需要很强的自制力,就能把英语学习坚持下来。		
查泰莱夫人的情人	航空工业	10.00

书名　介绍	版　别	定价
飘	航空工业	10.00
红与黑	航空工业	10.00
了不起的盖茨比	航空工业	10.00
歌剧魅影	航空工业	10.00
三个火枪手	航空工业	10.00
傲慢与偏见	航空工业	10.00
呼啸山庄	航空工业	10.00
简·爱	航空工业	10.00
儿子与情人	航空工业	10.00
床头灯英语学习读本 Ⅱ：		
鲁滨逊漂流记	航空工业	10.00
大战火星人	航空工业	10.00
巴斯克维尔猎犬	航空工业	10.00
时间机器	航空工业	10.00
远大前程	航空工业	10.00
彼得　潘	航空工业	10.00
格列佛游记	航空工业	10.00
黑骏马	航空工业	10.00
汤姆·索亚历险记	航空工业	10.00
杨柳风	航空工业	10.00
床头灯英语学习读本 Ⅲ：		
德伯家的苔丝	航空工业	10.00
化身博士	航空工业	10.00
野性的呼唤	航空工业	10.00

书名　介绍	版　别	定价
阿丽思漫游奇境记	航空工业	10.00
弗兰肯斯坦	航空工业	10.00
白鲸	航空工业	10.00
环游地球 80 天	航空工业	10.00
圣诞欢歌	航空工业	10.00
圣经故事	航空工业	10.00
希腊神话故事	航空工业	10.00
有声读物系列:		
最好的英文故事系列:		
猫咪凯蒂和小老鼠(音带版)(1 书 1 音带)	开明文教	15.00
猫咪凯蒂和小老鼠(CD 版)(1 书 1CD)	开明文教	16.00
兔山(音带版)(1 书 1 音带)	开明文教	15.00
兔山(CD 版)(1 书 1CD)	开明文教	16.00
爸爸和我(音带版)(1 书 1 音带)	开明文教	15.00
爸爸和我(CD 版)(1 书 1CD)	开明文教	16.00
又来了一只狗(音带版)(1 书 1 音带)	开明文教	15.00
又来了一只狗(CD 版)(1 书 1CD)	开明文教	16.00
动物和数字(音带版)(1 书 1 音带)	开明文教	15.00
动物和数字(CD 版)(1 书 1CD)	开明文教	16.00
考试虫英语美文选(书 1 本,音带 4 盒) 　　选文精,译文水平一流,美籍演员朗诵。	开明文教	36.00
正音——美语发音基本功(书 1 本,音带 2 盒) 　　一针见血地指出了中国人说英语的习惯性错误,采用针对中国人的矫治训练。中式发音→美式发音。	航空工业	24.00
正音——美语发音基本功	航空工业	10.00

书名　介绍	版　别	定价
正音——美语发音基本功(音带2盒)	开明文教	14.00
English Small Talk(英语小对话)(书1本,音带2盒) 　　由美国教育家丹尼斯夫妇为中国人写的口语书,语音地道、优美,是美国人现在讲的英语。由美国播音员和演员在美国录制。	开明文教	22.00/套
标准美国英语口语(音带版)(1书4带)	开明文教	32.00
标准美国英语口语(CD版)(1书4CD)	开明文教	36.00
英语听力基本功——听写训练①(书1本,音带2盒) 　　泰坦尼克号故事,语音纯正,优美,听起来是种享受。听写训练是提高听力的必由之路。本书是听力基础薄弱的同学之必读书。	开明文教	18.00
英语听力基本功——听写训练②(书1本,音带2盒) 　　THE BIG SPLASH故事,语音纯正,优美,听起来是种享受。	开明文教	18.00
国句名篇(书1本,CD、VCD各1张)(北京大学许渊冲教授汉诗英译精选) 　　翻译家许渊冲先生汉诗英译53首,精制成一张CD;英文朗诵:Kristopher Chung;中文朗诵:怀如(中央人民广播电台资深播音员),配乐:宋铁铮(中央台资深配乐);中央台节目东方之子——翻译家许渊冲(赠一张VCD)。	开明文教	22.00/套
最好的儿童英文歌曲(一)(书1本,音带2盒) 　　由美国教育家丹尼斯夫妇合编,音带中有原唱歌曲和丹尼斯朗诵的英文歌词,由中央台合成。	开明文教	22.00/套
最好的儿童英文歌曲(二)(书1本,音带2盒)	开明文教	22.00/套
最好的英文歌谣(书1本,音带2盒,彩印) 　　丹尼斯夫妇在美国花了近两年的时间收集编写的英文歌谣,由美国演员录音。从中不但可以学到地道的英文,而且可以了解英美文化。	开明文教	26.00/套

书名　介绍	版　别	定价
英文金曲赏析(精华版)(书1本,音带2盒) 　　中英文歌词与赏析、语言难点注释。音带里包含英文歌词朗诵和原声金曲,由中央台合成。	开明文教	22.00/套
英文金曲赏析(一)～(九)(书1本,音带2盒) 　　有位专家说,如果把这200首歌曲听透,那英文水平肯定会提高。	开明文教	22.00/辑
英文背诵圣典(一)～(五)(书1本,音带2盒) 　　小说、散文、电影、诗歌、演讲等名段及实用写作;音带:书中名篇的朗诵以及名曲配乐。	开明文教	18.00/辑
大学英语之声——《大学英语》2001年精华版(书1本,音带2盒)	开明文教	20.00
大学英语之声——《大学英语》2002年精华版(书1本,音带3盒)	北京电视艺术中心	26.00
考试虫英文电影课堂:		
音乐之声(音带版)(1书2带)	开明文教	22.00
音乐之声(CD版)(1书2CD)	开明文教	24.00
罗马假日(音带版)(1书2带)	开明文教	22.00
罗马假日(CD版)(1书2CD)	开明文教	24.00
简·爱(音带版)(1书2带)	开明文教	22.00
简·爱(CD版)(1书2CD)	开明文教	24.00
人鬼情未了(音带版)(1书2带)	开明文教	22.00
人鬼情未了(CD版)(1书2CD)	开明文教	24.00
魂断蓝桥(音带版)(1书2带)	开明文教	22.00
魂断蓝桥(CD版)(1书2CD)	开明文教	24.00
飘(音带版)(1书2带)	开明文教	22.00
飘(CD版)(1书2CD)	开明文教	24.00
廊桥遗梦(音带版)(1书2带)	开明文教	22.00

书名　介绍	版　别	定价
正音——美语发音基本功(音带2盒)	开明文教	14.00
English Small Talk(英语小对话)(书1本,音带2盒) 　　由美国教育家丹尼斯夫妇为中国人写的口语书,语音地道、优美,是美国人现在讲的英语。由美国播音员和演员在美国录制。	开明文教	22.00/套
标准美国英语口语(音带版)(1书4带)	开明文教	32.00
标准美国英语口语(CD版)(1书4CD)	开明文教	36.00
英语听力基本功——听写训练①(书1本,音带2盒) 　　泰坦尼克号故事,语音纯正,优美,听起来是种享受。听写训练是提高听力的必由之路。本书是听力基础薄弱的同学之必读书。	开明文教	18.00
英语听力基本功——听写训练②(书1本,音带2盒) 　　THE BIG SPLASH故事,语音纯正,优美,听起来是种享受。	开明文教	18.00
国句名篇(书1本,CD、VCD各1张)(北京大学许渊冲教授汉诗英译精选) 　　翻译家许渊冲先生汉诗英译53首,精制成一张 CD;英文朗诵:Kristopher Chung;中文朗诵:林如(中央人民广播电台资深播音员),配乐:宋铁铮(中央台资深配乐);中央台节目东方之子——翻译家许渊冲(赠一张 VCD)。	开明文教	22.00/套
最好的儿童英文歌曲(一)(书1本,音带2盒) 　　由美国教育家丹尼斯夫妇合编,音带中有原唱歌曲和丹尼斯朗诵的英文歌词,由中央台合成。	开明文教	22.00/套
最好的儿童英文歌曲(二)(书1本,音带2盒)	开明文教	22.00/套
最好的英文歌谣(书1本,音带2盒,彩印) 　　丹尼斯夫妇在美国花了近两年的时间收集编写的英文歌谣,由美国演员录音。从中不但可以学到地道的英文,而且可以了解英美文化。	开明文教	26.00/套

书名 介绍	版 别	定价
英文金曲赏析(精华版)(书1本,音带2盒) 　　中英文歌词与赏析、语言难点注释。音带里包含英文歌词朗诵和原声金曲,由中央台合成。	开明文教	22.00/套
英文金曲赏析(一)~(九)(书1本,音带2盒) 　　有位专家说,如果把这200首歌曲听透,那英文水平肯定会提高。	开明文教	22.00/辑
英文背诵圣典(一)~(五)(书1本,音带2盒) 　　小说、散文、电影、诗歌、演讲等名段及实用写作;音带:书中名篇的朗诵以及名曲配乐。	开明文教	18.00/辑
大学英语之声——《大学英语》2001 年精华版(书1本,音带2盒)	开明文教	20.00
大学英语之声——《大学英语》2002 年精华版(书1本,音带3盒)	北京电视艺术中心	26.00
考试虫英文电影课堂:		
音乐之声(音带版)(1书2带)	开明文教	22.00
音乐之声(CD版)(1书2CD)	开明文教	24.00
罗马假日(音带版)(1书2带)	开明文教	22.00
罗马假日(CD版)(1书2CD)	开明文教	24.00
简·爱(音带版)(1书2带)	开明文教	22.00
简·爱(CD版)(1书2CD)	开明文教	24.00
人鬼情未了(音带版)(1书2带)	开明文教	22.00
人鬼情未了(CD版)(1书2CD)	开明文教	24.00
魂断蓝桥(音带版)(1书2带)	开明文教	22.00
魂断蓝桥(CD版)(1书2CD)	开明文教	24.00
飘(音带版)(1书2带)	开明文教	22.00
飘(CD版)(1书2CD)	开明文教	24.00
廊桥遗梦(音带版)(1书2带)	开明文教	22.00

书名　介绍	版　别	定价
廊桥遗梦(CD版)(1 书 2CD)	开明文教	24.00
泰坦尼克号(音带版)(1 书 2 带)	开明文教	22.00
泰坦尼克号(CD版)(1 书 2CD)	开明文教	24.00
阿甘正传(音带版)(1 书 2 带)	开明文教	22.00
阿甘正传(CD版)(1 书 2CD)	开明文教	24.00
狮子王(音带版)(1 书 2 带)	开明文教	22.00
狮子王(CD版)(1 书 2CD) 　　通过英文原版电影学英语无疑是学英语的最好方法,但很多人弄不懂电影对白,本系列讲解部分不放过任何一个疑难之处,帮你彻底看懂电影。	开明文教	24.00

全国各大外文、新华、民营书店均有售。

销售咨询电话: 010－82863352　82867367　84841802

北京零售地址: 海淀西大街 36 号海淀图书城昊海楼 108 英汉达书店

　　　　　　电话:62534432

　　　　　　北京学考圆书店(北航北门斜对面)

　　　　　　电话:82381301

　　　　　　北京市海淀区学院路 9 号 109、228－230 号

　　　　　　电话: 82370959(60)　82370956

邮购地址: 北京市海淀区五道口华清嘉园 7 号楼 1501

　　　　　　邮购部(收)　　100083

电　　话: 010－82863351　82867367

邮购书免邮费,音带加收 5 元邮资(包装费)

售后服务电话: 010－82863393　13601002700　13601274554

E-mail: dy_wrx@etang.com

网　址: http://www.sinoexam.com 或在地址栏中输入"考试虫"回车
　　　　即可进入该网站(网络实名)

考试虫系列反馈意见调研表

书名：床头灯英语学习读本 I 　了不起的盖茨比

请将下面的问卷填好后寄至北京市海淀区清华南路华清商务会馆1501室(100083)王若平(收)；上网www.sinoexam.com或在地址栏里输入"考试虫"回车即可进入网站(网络实名)至王若平信箱；或E-mail至wrx1@vip.sina.com。

1. 您的个人资料：

　　姓名 _____ 性别 _____ 年龄 _____ 职业 _____

　　通讯地址 _____ 邮编 _____

　　E-mail _____ 电话 _____ 其它 _____

2. 对本书您最满意的是：

　　☐ 内容　　　　☐ 编校质量　　　☐ 版式设计　　　☐ 封面设计

　　☐ 印装质量　　☐ 所配音像制品的质量　　　　　　☐ 其它

3. 您认为本书的不足之处是：

4. 您的建议：

您的中肯建议，将得到特别奖励。